General Burgoyne

The Heiress

General Burgoyne

The Heiress

1st Edition | ISBN: 978-3-75238-296-9

Place of Publication: Frankfurt am Main, Germany

Year of Publication: 2020

Outlook Verlag GmbH, Germany.

Reproduction of the original.

THE HEIRESS

By GENERAL BURGOYNE.

REMARKS.

The author of this play was an elegant writer, and a brave soldier—yet, as an author he had faults, and as a general failures. His life was eventful; and he appears to have had, among his other qualities, that of patient philosophy: or if, in the warmth of youth, or pride of manhood, he was ever elated by prosperity, it is certain he bore adversity with cheerful resignation; that adversity, which is more formidable to the ambitious, than poverty to the luxurious—disappointment of expected renown.

Secret love, and clandestine marriage, composed the first acts of that tragicomedy, called his life. His cultivated mind, and endearing manners, reconciled, in a short time, the noble house of Derby to his stolen union with Lady Charlotte Stanley: her father, the late Earl of Derby, acknowledged him for his son-in-law; while the present Earl considered him, not only as his uncle, but his friend ı.

The author was, at that period, but a subaltern in the army. The patronage of his new relations, more than his own merit, it is probable, obtained him higher rank. He was, however, possessed of talents for a general, and those talents were occasionally rewarded with success. But his misfortunes in battle have been accompanied by circumstances more memorable than his victories —the latter were but of slight or partial consequence; his defeat at Saratoga was of great and direful import.

He sent an able, and most pathetic account, from America, of the surrender of his whole army—it was correctly written, and the style charmed every reader—but he had better have beaten the enemy, and mis-spelt every word of his dispatch; for so, probably, the great Duke of Marlborough would have done, both by one and the other.

General Burgoyne appears to have been a man capable of performing all things that did not require absolute genius. He was complete in mediocrity, A valiant, but not always a skilful, soldier; an elegant, but sometimes an insipid, writer.

When the comedy of "The Heiress" was first acted, it was compared, and preferred by some persons, to "The School for Scandal." It attracted vast sums of money from the east, as well as the west part of the metropolis;—but was more justly appreciated when the season of acting was over, and the playhouses closed.

Still, it is a production which claims high respect, from a degree of refinement which pervades the whole work; from the peculiar situation of its author; and from other circumstances closely connected with its performance on the stage.—"The Heiress" is dedicated to the Earl of Derby; and the present Countess of Derby was the Lady Emily of the drama when it was first acted.

The author, in his Preface, has, with much art, paid a deference to Miss Farren, by a compliment separate from her brother and sister performers; at the same time, wisely taking care not to excite their jealousy, while he soothed the partiality of his noble relation. He thanks and praises her merely for speaking his Epilogue, in which, of course, no other performer had a claim to his acknowledgments.

Lieutenant General Burgoyne is the author of another comedy, called "The Maid of the Oaks," and the excellent farce of "Bon Ton."—He was enamoured of the stage, and was at a play, in the little theatre of the Haymarket, the night previous to that on which he died suddenly, in the summer of 1792.

He was a Privy Counsellor, Colonel of the 4th regiment of foot, and Member of Parliament for Preston, in Lancashire. He had held many offices of great emolument; but having resigned them all about the time he wrote this comedy, he was at length rather a confirmation of, than an exception to, the adage—an author is seldom wealthy.

1 (return)
> The late Earl of Derby was grandfather to the present Earl, his son having died before him.

DRAMATIS PERSONÆ.

SIR CLEMENT FLINT	*Mr. King.*
CLIFFORD	*Mr. Smith.*
LORD GAYVILLE	*Mr. Palmer.*
ALSCRIP	*Mr. Parsons.*
CHIGNON	*Mr. Baddeley.*
MR. BLANDISH	*Mr. Bannister, jun.*
PROMPT	*Mr. R. Palmer.*
MR. RIGHTLY	*Mr. Aickin.*
LADY EMILY	*Miss Farren.*
MISS ALSCRIP	*Miss Pope.*
MISS ALTON	*Mrs. Crouch.*
MRS. SAGELY	*Mrs. Booth.*
TIFFANY	*Miss Tidswell.*
MRS. BLANDISH	*Mrs. Wilson.*
CHAIRMEN, SERVANTS, &c.	

SCENE—*London.*

4

ACT THE FIRST.

SCENE I.

A Lady's Apartment.

MR. BLANDISH *and* MRS. LETITIA BLANDISH *discovered writing: Letters folded up, and Message Cards scattered upon the Table.*

MRS. BLANDISH *leans upon her Elbows, as meditating; writes, as pleased with her Thought; lays down the Pen.*

Mrs. Blandish. There it is, complete——

[*Reads conceitedly.*

Adieu, my charming friend, my amiable, my all Accomplished associate! conceive the ardour of Your lovers united with your own sensibility— Still will the compound be but faintly expressive Of the truth and tenderness of your

LETITIA BLANDISH.

There's phrase—there's a period—match it, if you can.

Blandish. Not I, indeed: I am working upon a quite different plan: but, in the name of the old father of adulation, to whom is that perfect phrase addressed?

Mrs. Blandish. To one worth the pains, I can tell you—Miss Alscrip.

Blandish. What, sensibility to Miss Alscrip! My dear sister, this is too much, even in your own way: had you run changes upon her fortune, stocks, bonds, and mortgages; upon Lord Gayville's coronet at her feet, or forty other coronets, to make footballs of if she pleased,—it would have been plausible; but the quality you have selected——

Mrs. Blandish. Is one she has no pretensions to; therefore the flattery is more persuasive—that's my maxim.

Blandish. And mine also, but I don't try it quite so high—Sensibility to Miss Alscrip! you might as well have applied it to her uncle's pig-iron, from which she derives her first fifty thousand; or the harder heart of the old usurer, her father, from which she expects the second. But come, [*Rings.*] to the business of the morning.

5

Enter PROMPT.

Here, Prompt—send out the chairman with the billets and cards.—Have you any orders, madam?

Mrs. Blandish. [*Delivering her Letter.*] This to Miss Alscrip, with my impatient inquiries after her last night's rest, and that she shall have my personal salute in half an hour.—You take care to send to all the lying-in ladies?

Prompt. At their doors, madam, before the first load of straw.

Blandish. And to all great men that keep the house—whether for their own disorders, or those of the nation?

Prompt. To all, sir—their secretaries, and principal clerks.

Blandish. [*Aside to* PROMPT.] How goes on the business you have undertaken for Lord Gayville?

Prompt. I have conveyed his letter, and expect this morning to get an answer.

Blandish. He does not think me in the secret?

Prompt. Mercy forbid you should be!

[*Archly.*

Blandish. I should never forgive your meddling.

Prompt. Oh! never, never!

Blandish. [*Aloud.*] Well, dispatch——

Mrs. Blandish. Hold!—apropos, to the lying-in list—at Mrs. Barbara Winterbloom's, to inquire after the Angola kittens, and the last hatch of Java sparrows.

Prompt. [*Reading his Memorandum as he goes out.*] Ladies in the straw —ministers, &c.—old maids, cats, and sparrows: never had a better list of how d'ye's, since I had the honour to collect for the Blandish family.

[*Exit.*

Mrs. Blandish. These are the attentions that establish valuable friendships in female life. By adapting myself to the whims of one, submitting to the jest of another, assisting the little plots of a third, and taking part against the husbands with all, I am become an absolute essential in the polite world; the very soul of every fashionable party in town or country.

Blandish. The country! Pshaw! Time thrown away.

Mrs. Blandish. Time thrown away! As if women of fashion left London, to turn freckled shepherdesses.—No, no; cards, cards and backgammon, are the delights of rural life; and, slightly as you may think of my skill, at the year's end I am no inconsiderable sharer in the pin-money of my society.

Blandish. A paltry resource——Gambling is a damned trade, and I have done with it.

Mrs. Blandish. Indeed!

Blandish. Yes; 'twas high time.—The women don't pay; and as for the men, the age grows circumspect in proportion to its poverty. It's odds but one loses a character to establish a debt, and must fight a duel to obtain the payment. I have a thousand better plans, but two principal ones; and I am only at a loss which to chuse.

Mrs. Blandish. Out with them, I beseech you.

Blandish. Whether I shall marry my friend's intended bride, or his sister.

Mrs. Blandish. Marry his intended bride?—— What, pig-iron and usury?— Your opinion of her must advance your addresses admirably.

Blandish. My lord's opinion of her will advance them; he can't bear the sight of her, and, in defiance of his uncle, Sir Clement Flint's, eagerness for the match, is running mad after an adventure, which I, who am his confidant, shall keep going till I determine.—There's news for you.

Mrs. Blandish. And his sister, Lady Emily, the alternative! The first match in England, in beauty, wit, and accomplishment.

Blandish. Pooh! A fig for her personal charms; she will bring me connexion that would soon supply fortune; the other would bring fortune enough to make connexion unnecessary.

Mrs. Blandish. And as to the certainty of success with the one or the other

——

Blandish. Success!—Are they not women?—But I must away. And first for Lord Gayville, and his fellow student, Clifford.

Mrs. Blandish. Apropos! Look well to Clifford. Lady Emily and he were acquainted at the age of first impressions.

Blandish. I dare say he always meant to be the complete friend of the family; for, besides his design on Lady Emily, his game, I find, has been to work upon Lord Gayville's understanding; he thinks he must finally establish himself in his esteem, by inexorably opposing all his follies.—Poor simpleton!—Now, my touch of opposition goes only to enhance the value of my acquiescence. So adieu for the morning—You to Miss Alscrip, with an unction of flattery, fit for a house-painter's brush; I to Sir Clement, and his family, with a composition as delicate as ether, and to be applied with the point of a feather.

[*Going.*

Mrs. Blandish. Hark you, Blandish—a good wish before you go: To make your success complete, may you find but half your own vanity in those you have to work on!

Blandish. Thank you, my dear Letty; this is not the only tap you have hit me to-day, and you are right; for if you and I did not sometimes speak truth to each other, we should forget there was such a quality incident to the human mind.

[*Exeunt.*

SCENE II.

LORD GAYVILLE's Apartment.

Enter LORD GAYVILLE and MR. CLIFFORD.

Lord G. My dear Clifford, urge me no more. How can a man of your liberality of sentiment descend to be the advocate of my uncle's family avarice?

Cliff. My lord, you do not live for yourself. You have an ancient name and title to support.

Lord G. Preposterous policy! Whenever the father builds, games, or electioneers, the heir and title roust go to market. Oh, the happy families Sir Clement Flint will enumerate, where this practice has prevailed for centuries; and the estate been improved in every generation, though specifically spent by each individual!

Cliff. But you thought with him a month ago, and wrote with transport of the match—"Whenever I think of Miss Alscrip, visions of equipage and splendour, villas and hotels, the delights of independence and profuseness, dance in my imagination."

Lord G. It is true, I was that dissipated, fashionable wretch.

Cliff. Come, this reserve betrays a consciousness of having acted wrong: You would not hide what would give me pleasure: But I'll not be officious.

Lord G. Hear me without severity, and I'll tell you all. Such a woman, such

8

an assemblage of all that's lovely in the sex!——

Cliff. Well, but—the who, the how, the where?

Lord G. I met her walking, and alone; and, indeed, so humbly circumstanced as to carry a parcel in her own hand.

Cliff. I cannot but smile at this opening of your adventure.—But proceed.

Lord G. Her dress was such as a judicious painter would chuse to characterise modesty. But natural grace and elegance stole upon the observation, and, through the simplicity of a quaker, showed all we could conceive of a goddess. I gazed, and turned idolater.

Cliff. [*Smiling.*] You may as well finish the description in poetry at once; you are on the very verge of it.

Lord G. She was under the persecution of one of those beings peculiar to this town, who assume the name of gentlemen, upon the sole credentials of a boot, a switch, and round hat—the things that escape from counters and writing desks, to disturb public places, insult foreigners, and put modest women out of countenance. I had no difficulty in the rescue.

Cliff. And, having silenced the dragon, in the true spirit of chivalry, you conducted the damsel to her castle.

Lord G. The utmost I could obtain was leave to put her into a hackney coach, which I followed unperceived, and lodged her in the house of an obscure milliner, in a bye street, whose favour was soon conciliated by a few guineas. I almost lived in the house; and often, when I was not suspected to be there, passed whole hours listening to a voice, that would have captivated my very soul, though it had been her only attraction. At last——

Cliff. What is to follow?

Lord G. By the persuasions of the woman, who laughed at my scruples with an unknown girl, a lodger upon a second floor, I hid myself in the closet of her apartment: and the practised trader assured me, I had nothing to fear from the interruption of the family.

Cliff. Oh, for shame, my lord! whatever may be the end of your adventure, such means were very much below you.

Lord G. I confess it, and have been punished. Upon the discovery of me, fear, indignation, and resolution, agitated the whole frame of the sweet girl by turns.—I should as soon have committed sacrilege, as have offered an affront to her person.—Confused—overpowered—I stammered out a few incoherent words—Interest in her fortune—respect—entreaty of forgiveness—and left her, to detest me.

Cliff. You need go no farther. I meant to rally you, but your proceedings and emotion alarm me for your peace and honour. You are on a double precipice; on one side impelled by folly, on the other—

Lord G. Hold, Clifford, I am not prepared for so much admonition. Your tone is changed since our separation; you seem to drop the companion, and assume the governor.

Cliff. No, my lord, I scorn the sycophant, and assert the friend.

Enter SERVANT, *followed by* BLANDISH.

Serv. My lord, Mr. Blandish.

[*Exit.*

Cliff. [*Significantly.*] I hope every man will do the same.

Blandish. Mr. Clifford, do not let me drive you away—I want to learn your power to gain and to preserve dear Lord Gayville's esteem.

Cliff. [*With a seeming Effort to withdraw his Hand, which* BLANDISH *holds.*] Sir, you are quite accomplished to be an example.—

Blandish. I have been at your apartment, to look for you—we have been talking of you with Sir Clement—Lady Emily threw in her word.—

Cliff. [*Disengaging his Hand.*] Oh, sir, you make me too proud. [*Aside.*] Practised parasite!

[*Exit.*

Blandish. [*Aside.*] Sneering puppy.—— [*To* LORD GAYVILLE.] My lord, you seem disconcerted; has any thing new occurred?

Lord G. No, for there is nothing new in being disappointed in a friend.

Blandish. Have you told your story to Mr. Clifford?

Lord G. I have, and I might as well have told it to the cynic my uncle: he could not have discouraged or condemned me more.

Blandish. They are both in the right. I see things exactly as they do—but I have less fortitude, or more attachment than others:—The inclinations of the man, I love, are spells upon my opposition.

Lord G. Kind Blandish! you are the confidant I want.

Blandish. What has happened since your discovery in the closet?

Lord G. The lovely wanderer left her lodgings the next morning—but I have again found her—she is in a house of equal retirement, but of very different character, in the city, and inaccessible. I have wrote to her, and knowing her to be distressed, I have enclosed bank bills for two hundred pounds, the acceptance of which I have urged with all the delicacy I am master of, and, by Heaven! without a purpose of corruption.

Blandish. Two hundred pounds, and Lord Gayville's name—

Lord G. She has never known me, but by the name of Mr. Heartly. Since my ambition has been to be loved for my own sake, I have been jealous of my title.

Blandish. And pr'ythee by what diligence or chance, did Mr. Heartly trace his fugitive?

Lord G. By the acuteness of Mr. Prompt, your valet de chambre. You must pardon me for pressing into my service for this occasion, the fellow in the world fittest for it.—Here he comes.

Enter PROMPT.

Prompt. Are you alone, my lord?

[*Starts at seeing his Master.*

Lord G. Don't be afraid, Prompt—your peace is made.

Prompt. Then there is my return for your lordship's goodness. [*Giving the Letter.*] This letter was just now brought to the place appointed, by a porter.

Lord G. By a Cupid, honest Prompt, and these characters were engraved by the point of his arrow! [*Kissing the Superscription.*] "To ——— Heartly, Esq." Blandish, did you ever see any thing like it?

Blandish. If her style be equal to her hand-writing—

Lord G. If it be equal!—Infidel! you shall have proof directly. [*Opens the Letter precipitately.*] Hey-day! what the devil's here? my bills again, and no line—not a word—Death and disappointment, what's this!

Prompt. Gad it's well if she is not off again—'faith I never asked where the letter came from.

Lord G. Should you know the messenger again?

Prompt. I believe I should, my lord. For a Cupid he was somewhat in years, about six feet high, and a nose rather given to purple.

Lord G. Spare your wit, sir, till you find him.

Prompt. I have a shorter way—my life upon it I start her myself.

Blandish. And what is your device, sirrah!

11

Prompt. Lord, sir, nothing so easy as to bring every living creature in this town to the window: a tame bear, or a mad ox; two men, or two dogs fighting; a balloon in the air—(or tied up to the ceiling 'tis the same thing) make but noise enough, and out they come, first and second childhood, and every thing between—I am sure I shall know her by inspiration.

Lord G. Shall I describe her to you?

Prompt. No, my lord, time is too precious—I'll be at her last lodgings, and afterwards half the town over before your lordship will travel from her forehead to her chin.

Lord G. Away then, my good fellow. He cannot mistake her, for when she was formed, nature broke the mould.

[*Exit* PROMPT.

Blandish. Now for the blood of me, cannot I call that fellow back; it is absolute infatuation: Ah! I see how this will end.

Lord G. What are your apprehensions?

Blandish. That my ferret yonder will do his part completely; that I shall set all your uncle's doctrine at nought, and thus lend myself to this wild intrigue, till the girl is put into your arms.

Lord G. Propitious be the thought, my best friend—my uncle's doctrine! but advise me, how shall I keep my secret from him for the present? 'Faith, it is not very easy; Sir Clement is suspicion personified: his eye probes one's very thought.

Blandish. Your best chance would be to double your assiduities to Miss Alscrip. But then dissimulation is so mean a vice.—

Lord G. It is so indeed, and if I give into it for a moment, it is upon the determination of never being her husband. I may despise and offend a woman; but disgust would be no excuse for betraying her. Adieu, Blandish; if you see Prompt first, I trust to you for the quickest communication of intelligence.

Blandish. I am afraid you may—I cannot resist you. [*Exit* LORD GAYVILLE.] —Ah! wrong—wrong—wrong; I hope that exclamation is not lost. A blind compliance with a young man's passions is a poor plot upon his affections.

[*Exit.*

SCENE III.

Mrs. Sagely 's *House*.

Enter Mrs. Sagely and Miss Alton.

Mrs. Sagely. Indeed, Miss Alton, (since you are resolved to continue that name) you may bless yourself for finding me out in this wilderness.— Wilderness! this town is ten times more dangerous to youth and innocence: every man you meet is a wolf.

Miss Alton. Dear madam, I see you dwell upon my indiscretion in flying to London; but remember the safeguard I expected to find here. How cruel was the disappointment! how dangerous have been the consequences! I thought the chance happy that threw a retired lodging in my way: I was upon my guard against the other sex, but for my own to be treacherous to an unfortunate—could I expect it?

Mrs. Sagely. Suspect every body, if you would be safe—but most of all suspect yourself. Ah, my pretty truant—the heart, that is so violent in its aversions, is in sad danger of being the same in its affections, depend upon it.

Miss Alton. Let them spring from a just esteem, and you will absolve me: my aversion was to the character of the wretch I was threatened with—can you reprove me?

Mrs. Sagely. And tell me truly now; do you feel the same detestation for this worse character you have made acquaintance with? This rake—this abominable Heartly?——Ah, child, your look is suspicious.

Miss Alton. Madam, I have not a thought, that I will not sincerely lay open to you. Mr. Heartly is made to please, and to be avoided; I resent his attempts, and desire never to see him more—his discovery of me here; his letters, his offers have greatly alarmed me. I conjure you lose not an hour in placing me under the sort of protection I solicited.

Mrs. Sagely. If you are resolved, I believe I can serve you. Miss Alscrip, the great heiress, (you may have heard of the name in your family) has been inquiring among decayed gentry for a companion. She is too fine a lady to bear to be alone, and perhaps does not look to a husband's company as a certain dependence. Your musical talents will be a great recommendation— She is already apprized, and a line from me will introduce you.

Miss Alton. I will avail myself of your kindness immediately.

Prompt. [*Without.*] I tell you I have business with Mrs. Sagely—I must come in.

Mrs. Sagely. As I live here is an impudent fellow forcing himself into the passage!

Miss Alton. Oh Heaven! if Mr. Heartly should be behind!

Mrs. Sagely. Get into the back parlour; be he who he will, I'll warrant I protect you.

[*Exit* MISS ALTON.

Enter PROMPT. [*Looking about.*]

Mrs. Sagely. Who are you, sir? What are you looking for?

Prompt. Madam, I was looking——I was looking—for you.

Mrs. Sagely. Well, sir, and what do you want.

Prompt. [*Still prying about.*] Madam, I want——I want—I want—

Mrs. Sagely. To rob the house, perhaps.

Prompt. Just the contrary, Madam—to see that all is safe within it.—You have a treasure in your possession that I would not have lost for the world—A young lady.

Mrs. Sagely. Indeed!—begone about your business, friend—there are no young ladies to be spoke with here.

Prompt. Lord, madam, I don't desire to speak with her—My attentions go to ladies of the elder sort—I come to make proposals to you alone.

Mrs. Sagely. You make proposals to me? Did you know my late husband, sir?

Prompt. Husband! My good Mrs. Sagely—be at ease—I have no more views upon you, that way, than upon my grandmother—My proposals are of a quite different nature.

Mrs. Sagely. Of a different nature? Why you audacious varlet! Here, call a constable—

Prompt. Dear madam, how you continue to misunderstand me—I have a respect for you, that will set at nought all the personal temptations about you, depend upon it, powerful as they are—And as for the young lady, my purpose is only that you shall guard her safe.—I would offer you a pretty snug house in a pleasant quarter of the town, where you two would be much more commodiously lodged—the furniture new, and in the prettiest taste—A neat little sideboard of plate—a black boy, with a turban to wait upon you—

Mrs. Sagely. And for what purpose am I to be bribed? I am above it, sirrah. I have but a pittance, 'tis true, and heavy outgoings—My husband's decayed bookkeeper to maintain, and poor old Smiler, that so many years together drew our whole family in a chaise—Heavy charges—but by cutting off my luxuries, and stopping up a few windows, I can jog on, and scorn to be beholden to you, or him that sent you. [PROMPT *tries at the Door, and peeps through the Key-hole.*] What would the impertinent fellow be at now? Keep the door bolted, and don't stand in sight.

Prompt. [*Aside.*] Oh! oh!—She is here I find, and that's enough.——My good Mrs. Sagely—your humble servant—I would fain be better acquainted with you—in a modest way—but must wait, I see, a more happy hour. [*Aside, going out.*] When honesty and poverty do happen to meet, they grow so fond of each other's company, it is labour lost to try to separate them.

[*Exit.*

Mrs. Sagely. Shut the street door after him, and never let him in again.

Enter MISS ALTON, from the inner Room.

Miss Alton. For mercy, madam, let me begone immediately. I am very uneasy—I am certain Mr. Heartly is at the bottom of this.

Mrs. Sagely. I believe it, my dear, and now see the necessity of your removal. I'll write your letter—and Heaven protect you. Remember my warning, suspect yourself.

[*Exit.*

Miss Alton. In truth I will. I'll forget the forbearance of this profligate, and remember only his intentions. And is gratitude then suspicious? Painful lesson! A woman must not think herself secure because she has no bad impulse to fear: she must be upon her guard, lest her very best should betray her.

ACT THE SECOND.

SCENE I.

An Apartment in Sir Clement Flint's House.

Lady Emily Gayville and Clifford at Chess.

Sir Clement sitting at a Distance, pretending to read a Parchment, but slily observing them.

Lady E. Check—If you do not take care, you are gone the next move.

Cliff. I confess, Lady Emily, you are on the point of complete victory.

Lady E. Pooh, I would not give a farthing for victory without a more spirited defence.

Cliff. Then you must engage with those (if those there are) that do not find you irresistible.

Lady E. I could find a thousand such; but I'll engage with none whose triumph I could not submit to with pleasure.

Sir C. [*Apart.*] Pretty significant on both sides. I wonder how much farther it will go.

Lady E. Uncle, did you speak?

Sir C. [*Reading to himself.*] "And the parties to this indenture do farther covenant and agree, that all and every the said lands, tenements, and hereditaments—um—um."——How useful sometimes is ambiguity.

> [*Loud enough to be heard.*

Cliff. A very natural observation of Sir Clement's upon that long parchment.

> [*Pauses again upon the Chess-board.*

> [Lady Emily *looking pensively at his Face.*

Cliff. To what a dilemma have you reduced me, Lady Emily! If I advance, I perish by my temerity; and it is out of my power to retreat.

Sir C. [*Apart.*] Better and better! To talk in cipher is a curious faculty.

Cliff. Sir?

Sir C. [*Still reading.*] "In witness whereof the said parties have hereunto

interchangeably set their hands and seals, this——um—um—day of—um
——um——."

Lady E. [*Resuming an Air of Vivacity.*]   Come, I trifle with you too long
——There's your coup de grace——Uncle, I have conquered.

[*Both rising from the Table.*

Sir C. Niece, I do not doubt it——and in the style of the great proficients, without looking upon the board. Clifford, was not your mother's name Charlton?

[*Folding up the Parchment, and rising.*

Cliff. It was, sir.

Sir C. In looking over the writings Alscrip has sent me, preparatory to his daughter's settlement, I find mention of a conveyance from a Sir William Charlton, of Devonshire. Was he a relation?

Cliff. My grandfather, sir: The plunder of his fortune was one of the first materials for raising that of Mr. Alscrip, who was steward to Sir William's estate, then manager of his difficulties, and lastly his sole creditor.

Sir C. And no better monopoly than that of a needy man's distresses. Alscrip has had twenty such, or I should not have singled out his daughter to be Lord Gayville's wife.

Cliff. It is a compensation for my family losses, that in the event they will conduce to the interest of the man I most love.

Sir C. Heyday, Clifford!—take care—don't trench upon the Blandish— Your cue, you know, is sincerity.

Cliff. You seem to think, sir, there is no such quality. I doubt whether you believe there is an honest man in the world.

Sir C. You do me great injustice—several—several—and upon the old principle that—"honesty is the best policy."—Self-interest is the great end of life, says human nature—Honesty is a better agent than craft, says proverb.

Cliff. But as for ingenuous, or purely disinterested motives——

Sir C. Clifford, do you mean to laugh at me?

Cliff. What is your opinion, Lady Emily?

Lady E. [*Endeavouring again at Vivacity.*]   That there may be such: but it's odds they are troublesome or insipid. Pure ingenuousness, I take it, is a rugged sort of thing, which scarcely will bear the polish of common civility; and for disinterestedness—young people sometimes set out with it; but it is

17

like travelling upon a broken spring—one is glad to get it mended at the next stage.

Sir C. Emily, I protest you seem to study after me; proceed, child, and we will read together every character that comes in our way.

Lady E. Read one's acquaintance——delightful! What romances, novels, satires, and mock heroics present themselves to my imagination! Our young men are flimsy essays; old ones, political pamphlets; coquets, fugitive pieces; and fashionable beauties, a compilation of advertised perfumery, essence of pearl, milk of roses, and Olympian dew.——Lord, I should now and then though turn over an acquaintance with a sort of fear and trembling.

Cliff. How so?

Lady E. Lest one should pop unaware upon something one should not, like a naughty speech in an old comedy; but it is only skipping what would make one blush.

Sir C. Or if you did not skip, when a woman reads by herself, and to herself, there are wicked philosophers, who doubt whether her blushes are very troublesome.

Lady E. [*To* Sir Clement .] Do you know now that for that speech of yours—and for that saucy smile of yours, [*To* Clifford .] I am strongly tempted to read you both aloud!

Sir C. Come try——I'll be the first to open the book.

Lady E. A treatise of the Houyhnhnms, after the manner of Swift, tending to make us odious to ourselves, and to extract morose mirth from our imperfections.— [*Turning to* Clifford .] Contrasted with an exposition of ancient morality addressed to the moderns: a chimerical attempt upon an obsolete subject.

Sir C. Clifford! we must double down that page. And now we'll have a specimen of her Ladyship.

Lady E. I'll give it you myself, and with justice; Which is more than either of you would.

Sir C. And without skipping.

Lady E. Thus then; a light, airy, fantastic sketch of genteel manners as they are; with a little endeavour at what they ought to be—rather entertaining than instructive, not without art, but sparing in the use of it——

Sir C. But the passions, Emily. Do not forget what should stand in the foreground of a female treatise.

Lady E. They abound: but mixed and blended cleverly enough to prevent any from predominating; like the colours of a shot lutestring, that change as you look at it sideways or full: they are sometimes brightened by vivacity, and now and then subject to a shade of caprice—but meaning no ill—not afraid of a Critical Review: and thus, gentlemen, I present myself to you fresh from the press, and I hope not inelegantly bound.

Sir C. Altogether making a perfectly desirable companion for the closet: I am sure, Clifford, you will agree with me. Gad we are got into such a pleasant freedom with each other, it is a pity to separate while any curiosity remains in the company. Pr'ythee, Clifford, satisfy me a little as to your history. Old Lord Hardacre, if I am rightly informed, disinherited your father, his second son.

Cliff. For the very marriage we have been speaking of. The little fortune my father could call his own was sunk before his death, as a provision for my mother; upon an idea that whatever resentment he might personally have incurred, it would not be extended to an innocent offspring.

Sir C. A very silly confidence. How readily now, should you and I, Emily, have discovered in a sensible old man, the irreconcileable offence of a marriage of the passions——You understand me?

Lady E. Perfectly! [*Aside.*] Old petrifaction, your hints always speak forcibly.

Sir C. But your uncle, the present Lord, made amends?

Cliff. Amply. He offered to send me from Cambridge to an academy in Germany, to fit me for foreign service: Well judging that a cannon ball was a fair and quick provision for a poor relation.

Sir C. Upon my word I have known uncles less considerate.

Cliff. When Lord Gayville's friendship, and your indulgence, made me the companion of his travels, Lord Hardacre's undivided cares devolved upon my sister: whose whole independent possession, at my mother's death, was five hundred pounds——All our education had permitted that unhappy parent to lay by.

Lady E. Oh, for an act of justice and benevolence, to reconcile me to the odious man! Tell me this instant what did he do for Miss Clifford?

Cliff. He bestowed upon her forty pounds a-year, upon condition that she resided with one of his dependents in a remote county, to save the family from disgrace; and that allowance, when I heard last from her, he had threatened to withdraw upon her refusing a detestable match he had endeavoured to force upon her.

Lady E. Poor girl!

Sir C. Upon my word an interesting story, and told with pathetic effect.—Emily, you look grave, child.

Lady E. [*Aside.*] I shall not own it however. [*To him.*] For once, my dear uncle, you want your spectacles. My thoughts are on a diverting subject —My first visit to Miss Alscrip; to take a near view of that collection of charms destined to my happy brother.

Sir C. You need not go out of the room for that purpose. The schedule of an heiress's fortune is a compendium of her merits, and the true security for marriage happiness.

Lady E. I am sure I guess at your system—That union must be most wise, which has wealth to support it, and no affections to disturb it.

Sir C. Right.

Lady E. That makes a divorce the first promise of wedlock; and widowhood the best blessing of life; that separates the interest of husband, wife, and child——

Sir C. To establish the independent comfort of all——

Lady E. Upon the broad basis of family hatred. Excellent, my dear uncle, excellent indeed; and upon that principle, though the lady is likely to be your niece, and my sister, I am sure you will have no objection to my laughing at her a little.

Sir C. You'll be puzzled to make her more ridiculous than I think her. What is your plan?

Lady E. Why, though her pride is to be thought a leader in fashions, she is sometimes a servile copyist. Blandish tells me I am her principal model; and what is most provoking, she is intent upon catching my manner as well as my dress, which she exaggerates to an excess that vexes me. Now if she will take me in shade, I'll give her a new outline, I am resolved; and if I do not make her a caricature for a printshop——

Cliff. Will all this be strictly consistent with your goodnature, Lady Emily?

Lady E. No, nor I don't know when I shall do any thing consistent with it again, except leaving you two critics to a better subject than your humble servant.

[*Courtesies, and exit with a lively air.*

Sir C. Well, Clifford! What do you think of her?

Cliff. That when she professes ill-temper, she is a very awkward counterfeit.

Sir C. But her beauty, her wit, her improvement since you went abroad? I expected from a man of your age and taste, something more than a cold compliment upon her temper. Could not you, compatibly with the immaculate sincerity you profess, venture as far as admiration?

Cliff. I admire her, sir, as I do a bright star in the firmament, and consider the distance of both as equally immeasurable.

Sir C. [*Aside.*] Specious rogue! [*To him.*] Well, leave Emily then to be winked at through telescopes; and now to a matter of nearer observation—— What is Gayville doing?

Cliff. Every thing you desire, sir, I trust; but you know I have been at home only three days, and have hardly seen him since I came.

Sir C. Nor I neither; but I find he has profited wonderfully by foreign experience. After rambling half the world over without harm, he is caught, like a travelled woodcock, at his landing.

Cliff. If you suspect Lord Gayville of indiscretion, why do you not put him candidly to the test? I'll be bound for his ingenuousness not to withold any confession you may require.

Sir C. You may be right, but he'll confess more to you in an hour, than to me in a month, for all that; come, Clifford, look as you ought to do at your interest—Sift him—Watch him—You cannot guess how much you will make me your friend, and how grateful I may be if you will discover——

Cliff. Sir, you mistake the footing upon which Lord Gayville and I live—— I am often the partner of his thoughts, but never a spy upon his actions.

[*Bows and exit.*

Sir C. [*Alone.*] Well played Clifford! Good air and emphasis, and well suited to the trick of the scene.—He would do, if the practical part of deceit were as easy at his age, as discernment of it is at mine. Gayville and Emily, if they had not a vigilant guard, would be his sure prey; for they are examples of the generous affections coming to maturity with their stature; while suspicion, art, and interest are still dormant in the seed. I must employ Blandish in this business—A rascal of a different cast—Below Clifford in hypocrisy, but greatly above him in the scale of impudence. They shall both forward my ends, while they think they are pursuing their own. I shall ever be sure of a man's endeavours to serve me, while I hold out a lure to his knavery and interest.

[*Exit.*]

SCENE II.

An Antichamber.

Alscrip. [*Without.*] Dinner not ordered till seven o'clock—Bid the kitchen-maid get me some eggs and bacon. Plague, what with the time of dining and the French cookery, I am in the land of starvation, with half St. James's-Market upon my weekly bills.

Enter [while speaking the last Sentence.]

What a change have I made to please my unpleaseable daughter? Instead of my regular meal at Furnival's Inn, here am I transported to Berkeley-Square, to fast at Alscrip House, till my fine company come from their morning ride two hours after dark——Nay, it's worse, if I am carried among my great neighbours in Miss Alscrip's suite, as she calls it. My lady looks over me; my lord walks over me; and sets me in a little tottering cane chair, at the cold corner of the table—Though I have a mortgage upon the house and furniture, and arrears due of the whole interest. It's a pleasure though to be well dressed. My daughter maintains all fashions are founded in sense——Icod the tightness of my wig, and the stiffness of my cape, give me the sense of the pillory—Plaguy scanty about the hips too—And the breast something of a merrythought reversed—But there is some sense in that, for if one sex pares away in proportion where the other swells, we shall take up no more room in the world than we did before.

Enter a SERVANT.

Serv. Sir, Miss Alscrip wishes to see you.

Alscrip. Who is with her?

Serv. Only Mrs. Blandish, sir.

Alscrip. She must content herself with that company, till I have had my whet——Order up the eggs and bacon.

[*Exit.*]

SCENE III.

*MISS ALSCRIP discovered at her Toilet. CHIGNON, [her
Valet de Chambre,] dressing her Head. MRS.*

*Blandish sitting by, and holding a Box of
Diamond Pins.*

Miss Als. And so, Blandish, you really think that the introduction of Otahaite feathers in my trimming succeeded?

Mrs. Blandish. Oh, with the mixture of those charming Italian flowers, and the knots of pearl that gathered up the festoons, never any thing had so happy an effect——It put the whole ball-room out of humour. Monsieur Chignon, that pin a little more to the front.

Miss Als. And what did they say?

Mrs. Blandish. You know it is the first solicitude of my life to see the friend of my heart treated with justice. So when you stood up to dance, I got into the thick of the circle——Monsieur, don't you think this large diamond would be well placed just in the middle?

Chignon. Eh! non, madame; ce ne releve pas——Dat give no relief to de weight of de curl——Full in de front un gros bouton, von great nob of diamond! pardie ce seroit un accommodage à la Polyphême; de big eye of de geant in de centre of de forehead.

Miss Als. Chignon is right in point of taste, though not quite so happy in his allusions as he is sometimes.

Chignon. Ah! Madame, you have done von grande injure to my contrée: You go for von monthe, and bring avay all de good taste——At Paris——all von side——de diamond—de cap—de glance—de bon mot même—All von side, nothing direct à Paris.

Miss Als. [*Smiling at* Chignon *, and then turning to* Mrs. Blandish.] Well!——And so——

Mrs. Blandish. So it was all admiration! Elegant, says Lady Spite—it may do very well for Miss Alscrip, who never looks at expense. The dress of a bridal princess! cries Mrs. Scanty, and for one night's wear too!

Miss Als. Delightful! the very language I wished for——Oh, how charmingly apropos was my accident! did you see when my trimming in the passe-pied of a cotilion came luckily in contact with Billy Skim's great shoe-buckle—How it ripped away?

Mrs. Blandish. Did I see it?

Miss Als. One of the great feathers stuck fast on the shoe, and looked for all the world like the heel wing of a Mercury in a pantomime.

Mrs. Blandish. Oh! you witty creature, how you describe!

Miss Als. It was a most becoming rent!

Mrs. Blandish. And what a display of indifference; what an example for a woman of fortune, did you exhibit in the bustle of picking up the scattered fragments!

Miss Als. When the pearls were trundling about, and I insisted upon the company being no longer disturbed, but would leave what remained for fairy favours to the maid who swept the room. He! he! he! Do you think Lady Emily would have done that better?

Mrs. Blandish. Lady Emily? poor girl!—How soon must she submit to be the humble second of the family.

Miss Als. He! he! he! Do you sincerely think so, Blandish? And yet it would be strange if it were otherwise, for I could buy her ten times over.

Chignon. Madame, vat humeure vould you wear to-day?

Miss Als. Humour, Chignon? What am I dressed for now?

Chignon. The parfaite aimable, madam: but my bringing de point of de hair more down to de eye-brow, or adding a little blowse to de sides, I can give you de look severe, capricieuse—vat you please.

Miss Als. We'll put it off for half an hour, I am not quite decided. I was in the capricieuse yesterday—I believe I shall keep on the perfect amiable. [*Exit* CHIGNON .] Tiffany, take off my powdering gown——Ah! ho!—— How the wench tugs—do you think you are pulling off the coachman's greatcoat?

Mrs. Blandish. My dear amiable!—do not let that sweet temper be ruffled —Why will you not employ me in these little offices. Delicacy like yours should be waited upon by the softness of a sylph.

[*During this Speech exit* TIFFANY *peevishly.*

Miss Als. I am promised a creature to be about me out of the common way.

Mrs. Blandish. A new woman?

Miss Als. No; something to be raised much higher, and at the same time fitted better to receive one's ill-humour. An humble companion, well born, well educated, and perfectly dependent, is a most useful appurtenance in the best families.

Mrs. Blandish. Well, do not raise her to the rank of a friend, lest I should be jealous.

Miss Als. You may be perfectly secure—I shall take particular care that friendship shall be out of the question on both sides. I had once thought of a restoration of pages to sit in scarlet and silver (as one reads in former times) upon the forepart of the coach, and to hold up one's train—but I have a new male attendant in a valet de chambre, who has possession of my bust—My two women will have the charge from the point of the shoulder to the toe—So my person being provided for—the Countess of Gayville shall have an attendant to wait upon her mind.

Mrs. Blandish. I vow a most elegant and uncommon thought.

Miss Als. One that can pen a note in the familiar, the punctilious, or the witty—It's quite troublesome to be always writing wit for one's self—But above all, she is to have a talent for music.

Mrs. Blandish. Ay, your very soul is framed for harmony.

Miss Als. I have not quite determined what to call her—Governante of the private chamber, keeper of the boudoir, with a silver key at her breast——

Enter CHIGNON.

Chignon. Madame, a young lady beg to know if you be visible.

Miss Als. A young lady—It is not Lady Emily Gayville?

Chignon. Non, madam, but if you were absente, and I had the adjustment of her head, she would be the most charmante personne I did ever see.

Miss Als. Introduce her. [*Exit* CHIGNON.]   Who can this be?

Mrs. Blandish. Some woman of taste, to inquire your correspondent at Paris—or—

Enter MISS ALTON.

*MISS ALSCRIP courtesying respectfully; MISS
ALTON retiring disconcerted.*

Miss Als. Of taste indeed, by her appearance!—Who's in the antichamber? Why did they not open the folding doors?—Chignon, approach a fauteuil for the lady.

Miss Alton. Madam, I come!—

Miss Als. Madam, pray be seated—

Miss Alton. Excuse me, madam,—

Miss Als. Madam, I must beg—

Miss Alton. Madam, this letter will inform you how little pretension I have to the honours you are offering.

Miss Als. [Reads.] *Miss Alton, the bearer of this, is the person I recommended as worthy the honour of attending you as a companion.* [Eyes her scornfully.] *She is born a gentlewoman; I dare say her talents and good qualities will speak more in her favour, than any words I could use—I am, Madam, your most obedient—*um—um—. Blandish, was there ever such a mistake?

Mrs. Blandish. Oh! you dear, giddy, absent creature, what could you be thinking of?

Miss Als. Absent indeed. Chignon, give me the fauteuil; [*Throws herself into it.*] Young woman, where were you educated?

Miss Alton. Chiefly, madam, with my parents.

Miss Als. But finished, I take it for granted, at a country boarding school; for we have, *young ladies*, you know Blandish, *boarded and educated*, upon blue boards, in gold letters, in every village; with a strolling player for a dancing master, and a deserter from Dunkirk, to teach the French grammar.

Mrs. Blandish. How that genius of yours does paint! nothing escapes you— I dare say you have anticipated this young lady's story.

Miss Alton. It is very true, madam, my life can afford nothing to interest the curiosity of you two ladies; it has been too insignificant to merit your concern, and attended with no circumstances to excite your pleasantry.

Miss Als. [*Yawning.*] I hope, child, it will be attended with such for the future as will add to your own—I cannot bear a mope about me.—I am told you have a talent for music—can you touch that harp—It stands here as a piece of furniture, but I have a notion it is kept in tune, by the man who comes to wind up my clocks.

Miss Alton. Madam, I dare not disobey you. But I have been used to perform before a most partial audience; I am afraid strangers will think my talent too humble to be worthy attention.

SONG.

For tenderness framed in life's earliest day,

A parent's soft sorrows to mine led the way;

The lesson of pity was caught from her eye,

And ere words were my own, I spoke in a sigh.

The nightingale plunder'd, the mate-widow'd dove,

The warbled complaint of the suffering grove,

To youth as it ripened gave sentiment new,

The object still changing, the sympathy true.

Soft embers of passion yet rest in the glow—

A warmth of more pain may this breast never know!

Or if too indulgent the blessing I claim,

Let reason awaken, and govern the flame.

Miss Als. I declare not amiss, Blandish: only a little too plaintive—but I dare say she can play a country dance, when the enlivening is required—So, Miss Alton, you are welcome to my protection; and indeed I wish you to stay from this hour. My toilet being nearly finished, I shall have a horrid vacation till dinner.

Miss Alton. Madam, you do me great honour, and I very readily obey you.

Mrs. Blandish. I wish you joy, Miss Alton, of the most enviable situation a young person of elegant talents could be raised to. You and I will vie with each other, to prevent our dear countess ever knowing a melancholy hour. She has but one fault to correct—the giving way to the soft effusions of a too tender heart.

Enter SERVANT.

Serv. Madam, a letter——

Miss Als. It's big enough for a state packet—Oh! mercy, a petition—for Heaven's sake, Miss Alton, look it over. [MISS ALTON *reads.*] I should as soon read one of Lady Newchapel's methodist sermons—What does it contain?

Miss Alton. Madam, an uncommon series of calamities, which prudence could neither see, nor prevent: the reverse of a whole family from affluence and content to misery and imprisonment; and it adds, that the parties have the honour, remotely, to be allied to you.

Miss Als. Remote relations! ay, they always think one's made of money.

Enter another SERVANT.

2 *Serv.* A messenger, madam, from the animal repository, with the only puppy of the Peruvians, and the refusal at twenty guineas.

Miss Als. Twenty guineas! Were he to ask fifty, I must have him.

Mrs. Blandish. [*Offering to run out.*] I vow I'll give him the first kiss.

Miss Als. [*Stopping her.*] I'll swear you shan't.

Miss Alton. Madam, I was just finishing the petition.

Miss Als. It's throwing money away—But give him a crown.

[*Exit with* MRS. BLANDISH *striving which shall be first.*

Miss Alton. "The soft effusions of a too tender heart." The proof is excellent. That the covetous should be deaf to the miserable, I can conceive; but I should not have believed, if I had not seen, that a taste for profusion did not find its first indulgence in benevolence.

[*Exit.*

ACT THE THIRD.

SCENE I.

Miss Alscrip's Dressing-room.

Miss Alton, discovered.

Miss Alton. Thanks to Mrs. Blandish's inexhaustible talent for encomium, I shall be relieved from one part of a companion that my nature revolts at. But who comes here? It's well if I shall not be exposed to impertinences I was not aware of.

Enter Chignon.

Chignon. [*Aside.*] Ma foi, la voila—I will lose no time to pay my addresse—Now for de humble maniere, and de unperplex assurance of my contrée [*Bowing with a French shrug.*— Miss Alton *turning over Music Books.*] Mademoiselle, est-il permis? may I presume to offer you my profound homage [Miss Alton *not taking Notice.*] Mademoiselle—if you vill put your head into my hands, I vill give a distinction to your beauty, that shall make you and me de conversation of all de town.

Miss Alton. I request, Mr. Chignon, you will devote your ambition to your own part of the compliment.

Mr. Als. [*Without.*] Where is my daughter?

Miss Alton. Is that Mr. Alscrip's voice, Mr. Chignon? It's awkward for me to meet him before I'm introduced.

Chignon. Keep a little behind, mademoiselle; he vill only pashe de room— He vill not see through me.

Enter Alscrip.

Alscrip. Hah, my daughter gone already, but [*Sees* Chignon.] there's a new specimen of foreign vermin—A lady's valet de chambre—Taste for ever! —Now if I was to give the charge of my person to a waiting maid, they'd say I was indelicate. [*As he crosses the Stage,* Chignon *keeps sideling to intercept his Sight, and bowing as he looks towards him.*] What the devil is mounseer at? I thought all his agility lay in his fingers: what antics is the monkey practising? He twists and doubles himself as if he had a raree-show at his back.

Chignon. [*Aside.*] Be gar no raree-show for you, monsieur Alscrip, if I

29

can help.

Alscrip. [*Spying* Miss Alton.] Ah! ah! What have we got there? Monsieur, who is that?

Chignon. Sir, my lady wish to speak to you in her boudoir. She sent me to conduct you, sir.

Alscrip. [*Imitating.*] Yes, sir, but I will first conduct myself to this lady— Tell me this minute, who she is?

Chignon. Sir, she come to live here, companion to my lady—Mademoiselle study some musique—she must not be disturbed.

Alscrip. Get about your business, monsieur, or I'll disturb every comb in your head—Go tell my daughter to stay till I come to her. I shall give her companion some cautions against saucy Frenchmen, sirrah!

Chignon. [*Aside.*] Cautions! peste! you are subject a' cautions yourself— I suspecte you to be von old rake, but no ver dangerous rival.

[*Exit.*

Alscrip. [*To himself, and looking at her with his Glass.*] The devil is never tired of throwing baits in my way. [*She comes forward modestly.*] By all that's delicious! I must be better acquainted with her. [*He bows. She courtesies, the Music Book still in her Hand.*] But how to begin—My usual way of attacking my daughter's maids will never do.

Miss Alton. [*Aside.*] My situation is very embarrassing.

Alscrip. Beauteous stranger, give me leave to add my welcome to my daughter's. Since Alscrip House was established, she never brought any thing into it to please me before.

Miss Alton. [*A little confused.*] Sir, it is a great additional honour to that Miss Alscrip has done me, to be thought worthy so respectable a protection as yours.

Alscrip. I could furnish you with a better word than respectable. It sounds so distant, and my feelings have so little to do with cold respect—I never had such a desire—to make myself agreeable.

Miss Alton. [*Aside.*] A very strange old man. [*To him, more confused.*] Sir, you'll pardon me, I believe Miss Alscrip is waiting.

Alscrip. Don't be afraid, my dear, enchanting diffident (zounds, what a flutter am I in!) don't be afraid—my disposition, to be sure, is too susceptible; but then it is likewise so dove-like, so tender, and so innocent. Come, play me that tune, and enchant my ear, as you have done my eye.

Miss Alton. Sir, I wish to be excused, indeed it does not deserve your attention.

Alscrip. Not deserve it! I had rather hear you, than all the signoritininies together.—These are the strings to which my senses shall dance.

[*Sets the Harp.*

Miss Alton. Sir, it is to avoid the affectation of refusing what is so little worth asking for.

[*Takes the Harp and plays a Few Bars of a lively Air.*
Alscrip *kisses her Fingers with rapture.*

Alscrip. Oh! the sweet little twiddle-diddles!

Miss Alton. For shame, sir, what do you mean?

[Alscrip *gets hold of both her Hands and continues kissing her Fingers.*

Miss Alton. [*Struggling.*] Help!

Enter Miss Alscrip.

Miss Als. I wonder what my papa is doing all this time?

[*A short Pause—* Miss Alscrip *surprised.—* Miss Alton *confused.*
— Alscrip *puts his Hand to his Eye.*

Alscrip. Oh, child! I have got something in my eye, that makes me almost mad.—A little midge—believe.—'Gad, I caught hold of this young lady's hand in one of my twitches, and her nerves were as much in a flutter as if I had bit her.

Miss Als. [*Significantly.*] Yes, my dear papa, I perceive you have something in your eye, and I'll do my best to take it out immediately——Miss Alton, will you do me the favour to walk into the drawing room?

Miss Alton. I hope, madam, you will permit me, at a proper opportunity, to give my explanation of what has passed?

[*Retires.*

Miss Als. There's no occasion—Let it rest among the catalogue of wonders, like the Glastonbury thorn, that blooms at Christmas.——To be serious, papa, though I carried off your behaviour as well as I could, I am really shocked at it—A man of your years, and of a profession where the opinion of the world is of such consequence—

Alscrip. My dear Molly, have not I quitted the practice of attorney, and turned fine gentleman, to laugh at the world's opinion; or, had I not, do you

31

suppose the kiss of a pretty wench would hurt a lawyer? My dear Molly, if the fraternity had no other reflections to be afraid of!

Miss Als. Oh! hideous, Molly indeed! you ought to have forgot I had a christened name long ago; am not I going to be a countess? If you did not stint my fortune, by squand'ring yours away upon dirty trulls, I might be called your grace.

Alscrip. Spare your lectures, and you shall be called your highness, if you please.

Enter SERVANT.

Serv. Madam, Lady Emily Gayville is in her carriage in the street, will your ladyship be at home?

Miss Als. Yes, show her into the drawing room. [*Exit* SERVANT.] I entreat, sir, you will keep a little more guard upon your passions; consider the dignity of your house, and if you must be cooing, buy a French figurante.

[*Exit.*

Alscrip. Well said, my lady countess! well said, quality morals! What am I the better for burying a jealous wife? To be chicken pecked is a new persecution, more provoking than the old one—Oh Molly! Molly!—

[*Exit.*

SCENE II.

The Drawing Room.

MISS ALTON, alone.

Miss Alton. What perplexing scenes I already meet with in this house? I ought, however, to be contented in the security it affords against the attempts of Heartly. I am contented—But, O Clifford! It was hard to be left alone to the choice of distresses.

Enter CHIGNON, introducing LADY EMILY.

Chignon. My Lady Emily Gayville—Madame no here! Mademoiselle, announce, if you please, my lady.

Lady E. [*Aside.*] Did my ears deceive me? surely I heard the name of Clifford—and it escaped in an accent!—Pray, sir, who is that?

[*To* CHIGNON.

Chignon. Mademoiselle Alton, confidante of my lady, and next after me in her suite.

[*Examines her Head Dress impertinently.* MISS ALTON *with great modesty rises and puts her Work together.*

Lady E. There seems to be considerable difference in the decorum of her attendants. You need not stay, sir.

Chignon. [*As he goes out.*] Ma foi, sa tête est passable—her head may pass.

Lady E. [*Aside.*] How my heart beats with curiosity! [MISS ALTON *having disposed her things in her Work Bag, is retiring with a Courtesy.*] Miss Alton, I am in no haste. On the contrary, I think the occasion fortunate that allows me to begin an acquaintance with a person of so amiable an appearance. I don't know whether that pert foreigner has led me into an error —but without being too inquisitive, may I ask if you make any part of this family?

Miss Alton. Madam, I am under Miss Alscrip's protection: I imagine I am represented as her dependent: I am not ashamed of humble circumstances, that are not the consequences of indiscretion.

Lady E. That with such claims to respect you should be in any circumstances of humiliation, is a disgrace to the age we live in.

Miss Alton. Madam, my humiliation (if such it be) is just. Perhaps I have been too proud, and my heart required this self-correction. A life of retired industry might have been more pleasing to me; but an orphan—a stranger— ignorant and diffident, I preferred my present situation, as one less exposed to misrepresentation. [*Bell rings.*] I can no longer detain Miss Alscrip from the honour of receiving your ladyship.

[*A respectful Courtesy, and exit.*

Lady E. There is something strangely mysterious and affecting in all this ——what delicacy of sentiment—what softness of manners! and how well do these qualities accord with that sigh for Clifford! she has been proud—proud of what?—of Clifford's love. It is too plain. But then to account for her present condition?—He has betrayed and abandoned her—too plain again, I fear.—She talked too of a self-corrected heart—take example, Emily, and recall thine from an object, which it ought more than ever to renounce. But here come the Alscrip and her friend: lud! lud! lud! how shall I recover my spirits! I must attempt it, and if I lose my present thoughts in a trial of extravagance, be it of theirs or my own, it will be a happy expedient.

Enter MISS ALSCRIP and MRS. BLANDISH.

33

[MISS ALSCRIP *runs up to* LADY EMILY *and kisses her Forehead.*

Lady E. I ask your pardon, madam, for being so awkward, but I confess I did not expect so elevated a salute.

Miss Als. Dear Lady Emily, I had no notion of its not being universal. In France, the touch of the lips, just between the eyebrows, has been adopted for years.

Lady E. I perfectly acknowledge the propriety of the custom. It is almost the only spot of the face where the touch would not risk a confusion of complexions.

Miss Als. He! he! he! what a pretty thought!

Mrs. Blandish. How I have longed for this day!—Come, let me put an end to ceremony, and join the hands of the sweetest pair that ever nature and fortune marked for connexion.

[*Joins their Hands.*

Miss Als. Thank you, my good Blandish, though I was determined to break the ice, Lady Emily, in the first place I met you. But you were not at Lady Dovecourt's last night.

Lady E. [*Affectedly.*] No, I went home directly from the Opera: projected the revival of a cap: read a page in the trials of Temper; went to bed and dreamed I was Belinda in the Rape of the Lock.

Mrs. Blandish. Elegant creature!

Miss Als. [*Aside.*] I must have that air, if I die for it. [*Imitating.*] I too came home early; supped with my old gentleman; made him explain my marriage articles, dower, and heirs entail; read a page in a trial of divorce, and dreamed of a rose-colour equipage, with emblems, of Cupids issuing out of coronets.

Mrs. Blandish. Oh, you sweet twins of perfection——what equality in every thing! I have thought of a name for you—The Inseparable Inimitables.

Miss Als. I declare I shall like it exceedingly—one sees so few uncopied originals—the thing I cannot bear—

Lady E. Is vulgar imitation—I must catch the words from your mouth, to show you how we agree.

Miss Als. Exactly. Not that one wishes to be without affectation.

Lady E. Oh! mercy forbid!

Miss Als. But to catch a manner, and weave it, as I may say, into one's own

34

originality.

Mrs. Blandish. Pretty! pretty!

Lady E. That's the art—Lord, if one lived entirely upon one's own whims, who would not be run out in a twelvemonth?

Miss Als. Dear Lady Emily, don't you dote upon folly?

Lady E. To ecstacy. I only despair of seeing it well kept up.

Miss Als. I flatter myself there is no great danger of that.

Lady E. You are mistaken. We have, 'tis true, some examples of the extravaganza in high life, that no other country can match; but withal, many a false sister, that starts as one would think, in the very heyday of the fantastic, yet comes to a stand-still in the midst of the course.

Mrs. Blandish. Poor, spiritless creatures!

Lady E. Do you know there is more than one duchess who has been seen in the same carriage with her husband—like two doves in a basket, in the print of Conjugal Felicity; and another has been detected—I almost blush to name it—

Mrs. Blandish. Bless us! where? and how? and how?

Lady E. In nursing her own child!

Miss Als. Oh! barbarism!——For heaven's sake let us change the subject. You were mentioning a revived cap, Lady Emily; any thing of the Henry Quatre?

Lady E. Quite different. An English mob under the chin, and artless ringlets, in natural colour, that shall restore an admiration for Prior's Nut-brown Maid.

Miss Als. Horrid! shocking!

Lady E. Absolutely necessary. To be different from the rest of the world, we must now revert to nature: Make haste, or you have so much to undo, you will be left behind.

Miss Als. I dare say so. But who can vulgarize all at once? What will the French say?

Lady E. Oh, we shall have a new treaty for the interchange of fashions and follies, and then say, they will complain, as they do of other treaties, that we out manufactured them.

Miss Als. Fashions and follies! O what a charming contention!

Lady E. Yes, and one, thank Heaven, so perfectly well understood on both sides, that no counter declaration will be wanted to explain it.

Miss Als. [*With an affected drop of her Lip in her Laugh.*] He! he! he! he! he! he!

Lady E. My dear Miss Alscrip, what are you doing? I must correct you as I love you. Sure you must have observed the drop of the under lip is exploded since Lady Simpermode broke a tooth— [*Sets her Mouth affectedly.*] —I am preparing the cast of the lips for the ensuing winter——thus—It is to be called the Paphian mimp.

Miss Als. [*Imitating.*] I swear I think it pretty—I must try to get it.

Lady E. Nothing so easy. It is done by one cabalistical word, like a metamorphosis in the fairy tales. You have only, when before your glass, to keep pronouncing to yourself nimini-pimini—the lips cannot fail taking their plie.

Miss Als. Nimini—pimini—imini, mimini—oh, it's delightfully infantine— and so innocent, to be kissing one's own lips.

Lady E. You have it to a charm—does it not become her infinitely, Mrs. Blandish?

Mrs. Blandish. Our friend's features must succeed in every grace! but never so much as in a quick change of extremes.

Enter SERVANT.

Serv. Madam, Lord Gayville desires to know if you are at home?

Miss Als. A strange formality!

Lady E. [*Aside.*] No brother ever came more opportunely to a sister's relief, "I have fooled it to the top of my bent."

Miss Als. Desire Miss Alton to come to me. [*Exit SERVANT.*] Lady Emily, you must not blame me; I am supporting the cause of our sex, and must punish a lover for some late inattentions—I shall not see him.

Lady E. Oh cruel!

[*Sees* MISS ALTON.

Enter MISS ALTON.

Miss Alscrip, you have certainly the most elegant companion in the world.

Miss Als. Dear, do you think so? an ungain, dull sort of a body, in my mind; but we'll try her in the present business. Miss Alton, you must do me a

36

favour.—I want to plague my husband that is to be—you must take my part—you must double me like a second actress at Paris, when the first has the vapours.

Miss Alton. Really, madam, the task you would impose upon me—

Miss Als. Will be a great improvement to you, and quite right for me.—Don't be grave, Lady Emily— [*Whose attention is fixed on* Miss Alton.] Your brother's penance shall be short, and I'll take the reconciliation scene upon myself.

Lady E. [*Endeavouring to recover herself.*] I cannot but pity him; especially as I am sure, that do what you will, he will always regard you with the same eyes. And so, my sweet sister, I leave him to your mercy, and to that of your representative, whose disposition, if I have any judgment, is ill suited to a task of severity.

Mrs. Blandish. Dear Lady Emily, carry me away with you. When a lover is coming, it shall never be said I am in the way.

Lady E. [*Looking at* Miss Alton.—*Aside.*] What a painful suspense am I to suffer? another instant, and I shall betray myself—adieu, Miss Alscrip.

Miss Als. Call Lady Emily's servants.

Lady E. You sha'n't stir—remember nimini primini. I am at your orders.

[*Exit.*

Mrs. Blandish. I follow you, my sweet volatile. [*Coming back, and squeezing* Miss Alscrip *'s Hand, in a half whisper.*] She'd give her eyes, to be like you.

[*Exit.*

Miss Als. Now for it, Miss Alton—Only remember that you are doubling me, the woman he adores.

Miss Alton. Indeed, madam, I am quite incapable of executing your orders to your satisfaction. The utmost I can undertake is a short message.

Miss Als. Never fear. [*Knock at the Door.*] There he comes—Step aside, and I'll give you your very words.

[*Exeunt.*

Enter Lord Gayville, *conducted by a* Servant.

Lord G. So, now to get thorough this piece of drudgery. There's a meanness in my proceeding, and my compunction is just. Oh, the dear, lost possessor of my heart; lost, irrecoverably lost!

Enter Miss Alton, from the Bottom of the
Scene.

Miss Alton. A pretty employment I am sent upon!

Lord G. [*To himself.*] Could she but know the sacrifice I am ready to make!

Miss Alton. [*To herself.*] The very picture of a lover, if absence of mind marks one. It is unpleasant for me to interrupt a man I never saw, but I shall deliver my message very concisely.—My lord——

Lord G. [*Turning.*] Madam. [*Both start and stand in surprise.*] Astonishment! Miss Alton! my charming fugitive?

Miss Alton. How, Mr. Heartly—Lord Gayville!

Lord G. My joy and my surprise are alike unutterable. But I conjure you, madam, tell me by what strange circumstance do I meet you here?

Miss Alton. [*Aside.*] Now assist me, honest pride! assist me, resentment.

Lord G. You spoke to me—Did you know me?

Miss Alton. No otherwise, my lord, than as Miss Alscrip's lover. I had a message from her to your lordship.

Lord G. For Heaven's sake, madam, in what capacity?

Miss Alton. In one, my lord, not very much above the class of a servant.

Lord G. Impossible, sure! It is to place the brilliant below the foil—to make the inimitable work of nature secondary to art and defect.

Miss Alton. It is to take refuge in a situation that offers me security against suspicious obligation; against vile design; against the attempts of a seducer— It is to exercise the patience, that the will, and perhaps the favour, of Heaven meant to try.

Lord G. Cruel, cruel to yourself and me—Could I have had a happiness like that of assisting you against the injustice of fortune—and when to be thus degraded was the alternative?—

Miss Alton. My lord, it is fit I should be explicit. Reflect upon the language you have held to me; view the character in which you present yourself to this family; and then pronounce in whose breast we must look for a sense of degradation.

Lord G. In mine, and mine alone. I confess it—Hear nevertheless my defence—My actions are all the result of love. And culpable as I may seem, my conscience does not reproach me with——

Miss Alton. Oh, my lord, I readily believe you—You are above its reproaches—qualities, that are infamous and fatal, in one class of life, create applause and conscientious satisfaction in another.

Lord G. Infamous and fatal qualities! What means my lovely accuser?

Miss Alton. That to steal or stab is death in common life: but when one of your lordship's degree sets his hard heart upon the destruction of a woman, how glorious is his success! How consummate his triumph, when he can follow the theft of her affections by the murder of her honour.

*Enter M*ISS *A*LSCRIP *softly behind.*

Miss Als. I wonder how it goes on.

Lord G. Exalted! Adorable woman!

Miss Als. Adorable! Ay, I thought how 'twould be!

Lord G. Hear me! I conjure you—

Miss Als. Not a word, if she knows her business.

Miss Alton. My lord! I have heard too much.

Miss Als. Brava. I could not have played it better myself.

Lord G. Oh! Still more charming than severe.

[*Kneels.*

Miss Als. Humph! I hope he means me, though.

Lord G. The character in which you see me here makes me appear more odious to myself, if possible, than I am to you.

Miss Als. [*Behind.*] By all that's treacherous I doubt it.

Miss Alton. Desist, my lord——Miss Alscrip has a claim.——

Miss Als. Ay, now for it.

Lord G. By Heaven, she is my aversion. It is my family, on whom I am dependent, that has betrayed me into these cursed addresses.—Accept my contrition—pity a wretch struggling with the complicated torments of passion, shame, penitence and despair.

Miss Als. [*Comes forward—all stand confused.*] I never saw a part better doubled in my life!

Lord G. Confusion! What a light do I appear in to them both! How shall I redeem myself, even in my own opinion?

Miss Als. [*Looking at* LORD GAYVILLE.] Expressive dignity!— [*Looking*

39

at Miss Alton.]   Sweet simplicity! Amiable diffidence!——"She should execute my commands most awkwardly."

Lord G. [*Aside.*] There is but one way.— [*To* Miss Alscrip .] Madam, your sudden entrance has effected a discovery which with shame I confess ought to have been made before—The lady, who stands there, is in possession of my heart. If it is a crime to adore her, I am the most guilty wretch on earth —Pardon me if you can; my sincerity is painful to me—But in this crisis it is the only atonement I can offer.

[*Bows and exit.*

Miss Als. [*After a Pause.*] Admirable!—Perfect! The most finished declaration, I am convinced, that ever was made from beggarly nobility to the woman that was to make his fortune—the lady, who stands there—the lady— Madam—I am in patient expectation for the sincerity of your ladyship's atonement.

Miss Alton. I am confounded at the strange occurrences that have happened; but be assured you see in me an innocent and most unwilling rival.

Miss Als. Rival! better and better!—You—you give me uneasiness? You moppet—you coquet of the side table to catch the gawkey heir of the family, when he comes from school at Christmas—You—you you vile seducer of my good old honoured father; [*Cries—In a passion again.*] What, is my lady dumb? Hussy? Have you the insolence to hold your tongue?

Miss Alton. Madam, I just now offered to justify this scene; I thought it the part of duty to myself, and respect to you. But your behaviour has now left but one sentiment upon my mind.

Miss Als. And what is that, madam?

Miss Alton. [*With pointed expression.*]   Scorn.

[*Exit.*

Miss Als. Was there ever any thing like this before?—and to a woman of my fortune?—I to be robbed of a lover—and that a poor lord too—I'll have the act revived against witchcraft; I'll have the minx tried—I'll—I'll—I'll

——

[*Exit.*

SCENE III.

Alscrip's Room of Business.

ALSCRIP and RIGHTLY.

Rightly. Upon all these matters, Mr. Alscrip, I am authorized by my client, Sir Clement Flint, to agree. There remains nothing but your favouring me with the inspection of the Charlton title-deeds, and your daughter's settlements may be engrossed.

Alscrip. I cannot conceive, my friend Rightly, any such inspection to be requisite. Have not I been in constant quiet possession?

Rightly. Sir Clement insists upon it.

Alscrip. A client insist! and you, an old practitioner, suffer such a demur to your infallibility!—Ah! in my practice I had the sure means of disappointing such dabblers and divers into their own cases.

Rightly. How, pray?

Alscrip. I read his writings to him myself.—I was the best reader in Chancery-lane for setting the understanding at defiance—Drew breath but once in a quarter of an hour, always in the wrong place, and made a single sentence of six skins of parchment—Shall I give you a specimen?

Rightly. [*Smiling.*] I have no doubt of your talent.

Alscrip. Then return to Sir Clement, and follow my example.

Rightly. No, Mr. Alscrip, though I acknowledge your skill, I do not subscribe to your doctrine. The English law is the finest system of ethics, as well as government, that ever the world produced, and it cannot be too generally understood.

Alscrip. Law understood! Zounds! would you destroy the profession!

Rightly. No, I would raise it. Had every man of sense the knowledge of the theory, to which he is competent; the practice would revert to the purity of its institution, maintain the rights, and not promote the knavery, of mankind.

Alscrip. [*Aside.*] Plaguy odd maxims.—Sure he means to try me— [*To him.*] Brother Rightly, we know the world and are alone—I have locked the door.

[*In a half whisper.*

Rightly. A very useless precaution. I have not a principle nor a proceeding that I would not proclaim at Charing Cross.

Alscrip. [*Aside.*] No! then I'll pronounce you the most silly, or the most impudent fellow of the fraternity.

Rightly. But where are these writings? You can have no difficulty in laying

41

your hand upon them, for I perceive you keep things in a distinguished regularity.

Alscrip. Yes, I have distinct repositories for all papers, and especially title deeds—Some in drawers—Some in closets— [*Aside.*] and a few under ground.

Miss Als. [*Rattling at the Door.*] What makes you lock the door, sir? I must speak to you this instant.

Alscrip. One moment, child, and I'll be ready for you.

[*Turning again to* RIGHTLY *, as to dissuade him.*

Rightly. [*Coolly.*] If the thoughts of the wedding-day make any part of the young lady's impatience, you take a bad way, Mr. Alscrip, to satisfy it; for I tell you plainly our business cannot be completed till I see these writings.

Alscrip. [*Aside.*] Confound the old hound—how he sticks to his scent!

[MISS ALSCRIP *still at the Door.*

Alscrip. I am coming, I tell you. [*Opens a Bureau in a confused hurry, shuffles Papers about, puts one into* RIGHTLY *'s Hand.*] There, if this whim must be indulged, step into the next room—You, who know the material parts of a parchment lie in a nutshell, will look it over in ten minutes.

[*Puts him into another Room.*

Miss Als. I won't wait another instant, whatever you are about—Let me in

———

Alscrip. [*Opening the Door.*] Sex and vehemence! What is the matter now?

Enter MISS ALSCRIP *in the most violent emotion.*

Miss Als. So, sir; yes, sir; you have done finely by me indeed, you are a pattern for fathers—a precious match you had provided!

[*Walking about.*

Alscrip. What the devil's the matter?

Miss Als. [*Running on.*] I, that with 50,000 independent pounds, left myself in a father's hands—a thing unheard of, and waited for a husband with unparalleled patience till I was of age——

Alscrip. What the devil's the matter?

Miss Als. [*Following him about.*] I, that at fourteen might have married a French Marquis, my governess told me he was—for all he was her brother

Alscrip. 'Gad a mercy, governess——

Miss Als. And as for commoners, had not I the choice of the market? And the handsome Irish Colonel at Bath, that had carried off six heiresses before, for himself and friends, and would have found his way to Gretna-green blindfold!

Alscrip. [*Aside.*] 'Gad I wish you were there now, with all my heart—What the devil is at the bottom of all this?

Miss Als. Why, Lord Gayville is at the bottom—And your hussy, that you was so sweet upon this rooming, is at the bottom; a treacherous minx!—I sent her only for a little innocent diversion, as my double——

Alscrip. Your what?

Miss Als. Why, my double, to vex him.

Alscrip. Double! this is the most useless attendant you have had yet.—'Gad I'll start you single handed in the art of vexation against any ten women in England!

Miss Als. I caught them, just as I did you, with your——

Alscrip. Is that all? 'Gad I don't see much in that.

Miss Als. Not much? what, a woman of my fortune and accomplishments turned off—rejected—renounced——

Alscrip. How! renounced?—has he broke the contract?——Will you prove he has broke the contract?

Miss Als. Ay. Now, my dear papa, you take a tone that becomes you; now the blood of the Alscrips rises;—rises as it ought; you mean to fight him directly, don't you?

Alscrip. O yes, I'm his man—I'll show you a lawyer's challenge, sticks and staves, guns, swords, daggers, poinards, knives, scissors and bodkins. I'll put more weapons into a bit of paper, six inches square, than would stock the armory of the Tower.

Miss Als. Pistols!——Don't talk to me of any thing but pistols,—my dear papa, who shall be your second?

Alscrip. I'll have two——John Doe, and Richard Roe——as pretty fellows as any in England to see fair play, and as used to the differences of good company.—They shall greet him with their fieri facias——so don't be cast down, Molly, I'll answer for damages, to indemnify our loss of temper and reputation—he shall have a fi-fa before to-morrow night.

Miss Als. Fiery faces and damages—What does your Westminster-hall gibberish mean?—Are a woman's feelings to be satisfied with a fie-fa—you old insensible—you have no sense of family honour—no tender affections.

Alscrip. 'Gad you have enough for us both, when you want your father to be shot through the head—but stand out of the way, here's a species of family honour more necessary to be taken care of—If we were to go to law, this would be a precious set off against us. [*Takes up the Deed, as if to lock it up.*] This—why what the devil—I hope I don't see clear—Curse and confusion, I have given the wrong one—Here's fine work—Here's a blunder —Here's the effect of a woman's impetuosity.

Miss Als. Lord, what a fuss you are in: what is in the old trumpery scroll?

Alscrip. Plague and parchment, old Rightly will find what's in it, if I don't interrupt him—Mr. Rightly—Mr. Rightly—Mr. Rightly——

[*Going to the Door* RIGHTLY *went out at.*

Enter SERVANT.

Serv. Sir, Mr. Rightly is gone.

Alscrip. Gone! whither?

Serv. Home, I believe, sir——He came out at the door into the hall, and he bade me tell your honour you might depend upon his reading over the deed with particular care.

Alscrip. Fire and fury, my hat and cane— [*Exit* SERVANT .] Here, my hat and cane.

[*Stamps about.*

Miss Als. Sir, I expect before you come home—

Alscrip. Death and devils, expect to be ruined——this comes of listening to you——The sex hold the power of mischief by prescription—Zounds!— Mischief—Mischief—is the common law of womankind.

[*Exit in a rage.*

Miss Als. Mercy on us—I never saw him more provoked, even when my mother was alive!

[*Exit.*

ACT THE FOURTH.

SCENE I.

Alscrip's Room.

Chignon alone.

Chignon. Que diable veut dire tout ça——vat devil, all dis mean?— Monsieur Alscrip enragé——Mademoiselle Alscrip fly about like de dancing fury at de Opera——My littel musicienne, shut up, and in de absence of madame, I keep de key of de littel bastille——By gad, I vou'd rader have de custody of my pretty prisoniere than the whole college of cardinals——but vat have we here?

Enter Sir Clement and Clifford.

Sir C. [*Speaking to a* Servant.] Mr. Alscrip not at home, no matter we'll wait his return——The French valet de chambre [*To* Clifford.] —It may be of use to make acquaintance with him—Monsieur, how do you like this country?

Chignon. Ver good contrée, sire, by and bye—when you grow a little more poor.

Sir C. Is that a Parisian rule for improvement?

Chignon. Yes, sir, and we help you to follow our example—In good times you hang, and you drown—In bad time you will be like us.—Alway poor— alway gay—forget your politics—laugh at your grievances—take your snuff, vive la dissipation,—ver good country.

Sir C. Thanks for your kind advice, monsieur, you Frenchmen are so obliging, and so communicative to strangers——I hear there is a young lady come into this family—we don't exactly know in what capacity—could not you contrive that she should pass through this room—or—

Chignon. [*Aside.*] By gar here be one more old rake after de littel musicienne.

Sir C. Only for curiosity,—we never saw her, and have particular reasons—

[*Gives Money.*

Chignon. Ma foi, your reasons be ver expressive— [*Aside.*] —but vat devil shall I do—open the cage of my little Rosignol—my pretty nightingale —no. Chignon—no— [*Looking out.*] ah, hah; La Tiffany——Now for de

45

politique——be-gar I undertake your business—and make you de dupe of de performance.

Sir C. So—Clifford—There goes as disinterested a fellow now as any in Europe. But hark you—Can you yet guess the purpose for which I brought you here?

Cliff. I profess, sir, I am in the dark. If it concerns Lord Gayville's secret.

Sir C. Namely, that this dulcinea has started up in the shape of Miss Alscrip's musical companion—Her name is Alton. [*Leering.*] I tell it you, because I am sure you are not acquainted with it.

Cliff. Sir, you will not know me.—

Sir C. Tut, tut, don't do me such injustice——Come, all delicacy being over, by my having made the discovery, will you talk to this girl?

Cliff. For what end, sir?

Sir C. If you state yourself as Lord Gayville's friend, she will converse with you more readily, than she would with me—Try her—find out what she is really at. If she has no hold upon him but her person, I shall be easy.

Cliff. Sir, let my compliance convince you how much I wish to oblige you. If I can get a sight of this wonder, I promise to give you my faithful opinion of my friend's danger.

Enter Chignon, *and makes a sign to* Sir Clement, *that the Person he inquired after is coming.*

Sir C. Leave her with this gentleman——Come, monsieur, you shall show me the new room.

[*Exit.*

Chignon. [*Aside.*] Vid dis gentleman—Vid all my heart—La Tiffany vill answer his purpose, and mine too.

[*Exit.*

[Clifford *is looking at the Furniture of the Room.*

Enter Tiffany.

Tiff. What does the Frenchman mean by gentlemen wanting me, and his gibberish of making soft eyes——I hope I know the exercise of my eyes without his instruction—hah! I vow, a clever looking man.

Cliff. 'Faith, a pretty attracting countenance—but for that apprehensive and timid look—that awe impressing modesty, my friend so forcibly described. [Tiffany *adjusts herself, and pulls up.*] — [*Aside.*] Her silence marks diffidence; deuce take me if I know how to begin, for fear of offending her reserve.

Tiff. [*Aside.*] I have been told pertness became me—I'll try, I'm resolved. [*To him.*] I hear, sir, you had something to say to a young person in this house—that—that— [*Looking down at the same time archly.*] I could not but take the description to myself—I am ready to hear any thing a gentleman has to say.

Cliff. [*Aside.*] Thank my stars, my scruples are relieved!

Tiff. Am I mistaken, sir? Pray, whom was you inquiring after?

Cliff. Oh! certainly you, my pretty stranger. A friend of mine has been robbed of his heart, and I see the felony in your looks. Will you confess, or must I arrest you?

Tiff. Innocent, sir, in fact, but not quite so in inclination—I hope your own is safe?

Cliff. And were it not, my smart unconscionable, would you run away with that also?

Tiff. Oh, yes, and a hundred more; and melt them all down together, as the Jews do stolen goods, to prevent their being reclaimed.

Cliff. [*Aside.*] Astonishing! Have I hit upon the moment when her fancy outruns her art! But are you really the young lady, that's admitted into this family, as companion to Miss Alscrip?

Tiff. Sir, if you mean the young lady, who, however undeservingly, is flatteringly called the flower of this family—who sometimes extracts notice from these windows; and to be sure has been followed home by gentlemen against her inclinations—sir, you are not mistaken.

Cliff. [*Aside.*] Sure it has been Gayville's madness or amusement then to describe her by contraries.

Tiff. I hope, sir, you are not offended? I would not be impertinent, though I am not so tasteless as to be shy.

Cliff. Offended, my dear? I am quite charmed, I assure you. And so without further shyness on either part, let us be free upon the subject I had to talk over with you. You surely are not looking to lasting connexions?

Tiff. [*With airs.*] Sir, I don't understand you—I am not what you suppose,

I assure you—Connexions indeed—I should never have thought of that—my character—my behaviour; connexions, I don't know what the word signifies.

Sir C. [*Without.*] Clifford—are you ready?

Cliff. I am at your orders, sir.

Tiff. [*Aside.*] Deuce take this interruption!

Sir Clement. [*Without.*] I shall not wait for Mr. Alscrip any longer.

Tiff. [*Aside.*] Lud, lud, he, gives me no time to come round again. [*Runs up to him confusedly.*] It's very true, sir, I would not do such a thing for the world, but you are a man of honour, and I am sure would not give bad advice to a poor girl who is but a novice—and so, sir, [*Hears* Sir Clement *entering.*] put your proposal in writing, and you may depend on having an answer.

[*Runs out.*

Enter Sir Clement.

Sir C. Well, Clifford, what do you think of her?

Cliff. Make yourself perfectly easy, sir: This girl, when known, can make no impression on Lord Gayville's mind; and I doubt not but a silk-gown and a lottery-ticket, had they been offered as an ultimatum, would have purchased her person.

Sir C. [*With a dry sneer.*] Don't you sometimes Clifford, form erroneous opinions of people's pretensions? Interest and foolish passion inspire strange notions—as one or the other prevails, we are brought to look so low, or so high—

Cliff. [*With emotion.*] That we are compelled to call reason and honour to our aid——

Sir C. And then——

Cliff. We lose the intemperance of our inclinations in the sense of what is right.

Sir C. [*Aside.*] Sententious impostor!— [*To him.*] But to the point.

Cliff. Sir, I would please you if I could—I am thinking of a scheme to restore Lord Gayville to his senses, without violence or injury to any one of the parties.

Sir C. Let me hear it.

Cliff. Why, the wench being cut short of marketing by word of mouth,

48

desired me to write proposals. I am inclined to do so. We will show the answer to Lord Gayville, and, depend upon it, there will be character enough displayed to cure him of the sentimental part of his attachment.

Sir. C. I like your idea—Sit down, and put it into execution immediately —— [CLIFFORD *writes.*] —— [*To himself.*] He is quick at invention—has a pretty turn at profession—A proud and peremptory show of honour would overpower prejudices. Thank Heaven, my opinions of knavery are convictions!

Cliff. [*Writing.*] I am sorry to detain you, sir.

Sir C. [*Looking at the Furniture.*] Oh! I am amusing myself better than you think—Indulging an edifying contemplation among the tombs of departed estates— [*Looking round the Furniture, viz. Closets, that show old Writings, tied up; Shelves with Boxes, labelled Mortgages, Lease and Release, &c.*] What mouldered skins, that will never see day-light again, and that, with a good herald, would vie with Westminster Abbey in holiday entertainment. For instance, now, what have we here?—Hah! The last remains of Fatland Priory —Once of great monastic importance: A proverb of pride, sloth, and hypocrisy. After the Reformation, the seat of old English hospitality and benevolence—In the present century, altered, adorned, pulled down, and the materials sold by auction.

Cliff. Edifying, indeed, sir; your comments are not lost.

Sir C. Here lie, undisturbed, in dust, the relics of Court Baron Castle, granted, at the Conquest, to the family of Loftimount. The last of this ancient race, having won twenty-seven king's plates, and represented the county in six parliaments, after many struggles, died of the pistol fever. A disconsolate annuitant inscribed this box to his memory.—Well, Clifford, have you done?

Cliff. Yes, sir.

[*Reads, as if to himself.*

You have captivated a young man of rank and fortune, but you are discovered, and his ruin and yours would be the consequence of pursuing any designs, that could impede his proposed marriage with Miss Alscrip.—Throw yourself upon the generosity of his family, and your fortune's made.—Send your answer (and let it be immediate) to me, at Sir Clement Flint's house.

Yours, &c. &c.

HENRY CLIFFORD.

[CLIFFORD *folds the Letter.*

Sir C. Our French friend is the man to deliver it, and to bring the answer. I am going home; you'll overtake me.

[Exit.

Enter CHIGNON.

Cliff. [*Sealing the Letter.*] You come apropos, monsieur. [*Gives the Letter with an Air of Mystery.*] Have the goodness to put this letter into Miss Alton's own hands.

Chignon. [*To himself.*] Mademoiselle Alton! Peste! My trick has not passed.

Cliff. To Miss Alton by herself—I am in all the secret.

Chignon. [*To himself.*] Devil take Tiffany, for making you so wise.

Cliff. And you serve your lady, when you serve me with Miss Alton— Monsieur, an answer as quick as possible—You will find me at Sir Clement Flint's—it is only in the next street—and—you understand me— [*Shaking his Purse.*] —Alerte, monsieur.

[Exit.

Chignon. Understand you!—Oui da! you talk de language universal. [*Imitating his shaking the Purse.*] J'entre vois, I begin to see something— By gad, I vill give de letter, ami try de inclination of Mademoiselle la Musicienne—if dis be de duette she vill play, it take her out of the vay of Alscrip, of Gayville, and of myself also—Voila le malheur—there—de misfortune—eh bien—when love and interest come across—alway prefer de interest for to-day, and take de chance of de love to-morrow—dat is de humour of France.

[Exit.

SCENE II.

SIR CLEMENT FLINT's House.

Enter LORD GAYVILLE and SIR CLEMENT.

Lord G. I am resolved to see Miss Alscrip no more.

Sir C. And I hope you are prepared with arguments to justify the cause of this breach, to me, and to the world.

Lord G. For my reconciliation with you, I hope your former partiality will return to my aid; and as for the world, I despise it. The multitude look at happiness through the false glare of wealth and pomp: I have discovered it, though yet at a distance, through the only true medium, that of mutual affection.

50

Sir C. No common place book, formed from a whole library of plays and novels, could furnish a better sentence. Your folly would shame a school-boy —even of the last age—In the present, he learns the world with his grammar, and gets a just notion of the worthlessness of the other sex, before he is of an age to be duped by their attractions.

Lord G. Sir, your prejudices——

Sir C. My prejudices?—will you appeal to Clifford—here he comes—your friend—your other self.

Enter CLIFFORD.

Lord G. And will Clifford condemn the choice of the heart?

Cliff. Never, my lord, when justly placed—In the case I perceive you are arguing, I am ready to blush for you—nay, don't look grave—I am acquainted with your enchantress.

Lord G. You acquainted with her?

Cliff. Yes; and, if I don't deceive myself, shall make her break her own spell. I am in correspondence with her.

Lord G. You in correspondence with Miss Alton!—when? where? What am I to think of this?

Cliff. My dear lord, that she is the most arrant coquette, the most accomplished jilt, the most ready trafficker of her charms——

Lord G. Phrensy and profanation!

Sir C. Come, Gayville, I'll be plain with you; you have sillily let the girl raise her price upon you—but, if nothing else will satisfy you, e'en pay it, and have done with her.

Lord G. Sir, her price is an unadulterated heart: I am afraid we cannot pay it betwixt us.

Enter CHIGNON; *he delivers a Letter to*
CLIFFORD, *apart.*

Chignon. Alerte, monsieur, I repete your word—Mademoiselle Alton be all your own.

Sir C. Come, Clifford, the contents: his lordship braves the trial.

Lord G. What is this mighty scheme! and what is that paper to discover?

Cliff. [*Breaking open the Letter.*] Your lordship shall be informed word for word. [*Upon first sight of the Contents he shows the utmost emotion.*]

Amazement! do I dream! can it be? who wrote this letter?

Sir C. Oh! speak out, monsieur, we are all friends.

Chignon. De true Mademoiselle Alton, whom you charge me to give your letter—she open it—she turn pale—den red—den confuse—den kiss your name—den write, and bid me fly.

Lord G. Confusion on confusion, what does all this mean? explain.

Cliff. You must pardon me, I am disconcerted—confounded—thunderstruck —This letter is indeed of a different nature, from that I expected—I am more interested in Miss Alton's fate than your lordship—my perplexity is not to be endured; friend, come with me instantly.

           [*Exeunt* CLIFFORD *and* CHIGNON.

Lord G. Mystery and torture! what am I to collect from this? He interested in the fate of Miss Alton? he her former acquaintance?

Sir C. Why not—and her dupe also?

        Enter a SERVANT.

Serv. Is Mr. Clifford gone, sir?

Lord G. [*Impatiently.*] Who wants him?

Serv. A chairman with a letter, he will not deliver to a servant.

Sir C. Call the fellow in. [*Exit* SERVANT.] Who knows but he may help us in our difficulties?

    CHAIRMAN *brought in, with a Letter in his*
         Hand.

Lord G. [*Still impatiently.*] Whom did you bring that letter from?

Chairman. Please your honour, I don't know; passing through the square, a sash flew up, and down came this letter and half a crown upon my head. It could not have fallen better, there's not a fellow in town more handy than I am, nor, though I say it more cute at private business—So I resolved to deliver it safely—Is your honour's name Clifford?

Lord G. No, indeed, friend, I am not so happy a man.

Sir C. [*Aside.*] That letter must not be lost though. Here, my friend—I'll take charge of your letter. [*Takes the Letter.*] Something for your pains.

Chairman. God bless your honour, and if you want to send an answer, my number is forty-seven in Bond Street—your honour, I am known by the name of secret Tom.

Lord G. What is the use of this deceit? strong as my suspicion is, a seal must be sacred.

Sir C. Our circumstances make an exception to your rule: when there is treason in the state, wax gives way. [*Takes the Letter, opens and reads it.*] 'Faith, this is beyond my expectation—though the mystery is unfathomable, the aptness of it to my purpose is admirable—Gayville—I wish you joy.

Lord G. Of what?

Sir C. Of conviction! if this is not plain! only hear. [*Reads.*] *Since my confused lines of a few minutes past, my perplexities redouble upon my spirits —I am in momentary apprehension of farther insult from the Alscrip family; I am still more anxious to avoid Lord Gayville,* [Pauses and looks at Lord Gayville.] *do not suspect my sincerity—I have not a thought of him that ought to disturb you.*—Here she is, Gayville, look at her, through the true medium of mutual affection—*I have not a thought of him that might to disturb you—Fly to me, secure me, my dearest Henry.*

Lord G. Dearest Henry!

Sir C. [Reads on.] *Dearest Henry—In this call, the danger of your Harriet unites with the impatience of her affection.*

Lord G. Hell, and fury! this must be some trick, some forgery. [*Snatches the Letter.*] —No, by all that's perfidious, it is that exquisite hand, that baffles imitation.

Sir C. All, regular, strict, undeviating modern morals—common property is the first principle of friendship; your horse, your house, your purse, your mistress—nay, your wife, would be a better example still of the doctrine of this generous age. Bless fortune, Gayville, that has brought the fidelity of your friend and your girl to the test at the same time.

Lord G. Sir, I am not in a humour for any spleen but my own. What can this mean? It must have been a secret attachment for years—but then the avowal of a correspondence, and the confusion at receiving it—his coldness in traducing her; the passionate interest he expressed in her fate; the conviction of his second letter—It is all delirium. I'll search the matter to the bottom, though I go to Clifford's heart for it.

[*Exit in great anger.*

Sir C. I'll after the precious fellow too—He is a rogue above my hopes, and the intricacy of his snares excite my curiosity.

[*Exit.*

SCENE III.

Lady Emily's Apartment.

Lady Emily discovered, reading.

Lady E. It will not do. My eyes may run over a thousand subjects, but my thoughts centre in one. Ah! that sigh! that sigh from the fair sufferer this morning——I have found it echo in my own heart ever since.

Enter Servant.

Serv. Madam, Mr. Blandish.

Lady E. Pooh! did you say I was at home?

Serv. Your ladyship gave no orders to the contrary.

Lady E. Show him in. [*Exit Servant .*] I must take up my air of levity again—It is the only humour for a fellow who I sometimes allow to entertain me, but who can never get my esteem. I have more calls upon my affection this unlucky day, than my real disposition would execute in a long life.

Enter Blandish.

Lady E. Blandish, I am horridly peevish; have you any thing new to divert me?

Blandish. If you ask me for news, the latest is, that Clifford has been detected in a clandestine intercourse with the object of Lord Gayville's secret passion; that he has betrayed the confidence of his friend and patron, and actually carried her off. [*Aside.*] Which, Gayville knows by this time, with all its aggravations, or Prompt has not been as active as he used to be.

Lady E. [*With Emotion.*] Blandish, this is a poor project. Clifford treacherous to his friend? You might as soon make me believe Gayville dispassionate, my uncle charitable, or you ingenuous.

Blandish. His conduct does not rest upon opinion, but proof; and when you know it, you must think of him with aversion.

Lady E. Must I? Then don't let me hear a word more—I have aversions enough already—

[*Peevishly.*

Blandish. It is impossible you can apply that word to one whose only offence is to adore you.

[*Kisses her Hand.*

54

Enter CLIFFORD.

Cliff. [*Aside, surprised.*] Blandish so favoured?

Lady E. [*Aside.*] Perverse accident: what mistakes now will he make!

Blandish. [*Aside.*] The enemy has surprised me—but the only remedy in such emergences, is to show a good countenance.

Cliff. I fear I have been guilty of an unpardonable intrusion.

Blandish. Mr. Clifford never can intrude; but though you had not come so apropos yourself—Lady Emily will bear testimony, I have not spared my pains to remove any prejudices she might have entertained.

Lady E. Had you not better repeat in your own words, Mr. Blandish, all the obliging things you have said of this gentleman?

Cliff. It is not necessary, madam—if without robbing you of moments that I perceive are precious—

Lady E. Sir?

Cliff. I might obtain a short audience—

[*Looking at* BLANDISH.

Blandish. [*Aside.*] He's devilish impudent—but he cannot soon get over facts, and I'll take care the conference shall not be long. [*To* LADY EMILY.] —Lady Emily; hear Mr. Clifford, and judge if I have misrepresented him — [*To* CLIFFORD.] When you want a friend, you know where to find him.

[*Exit.*

Lady E. This is an interview, Mr. Clifford, that I desire not to be understood to have authorized. It is not to me, you are accountable for your actions—I have no personal interest in them.

Cliff. I know it well.

Lady E. [*Peevishly.*] Do not run away with the notion neither, that I am therefore interested in any other person's—You have among you vexed and disconcerted me, but there is not a grain of partiality in all my embarrassment —if you have any eyes, you may see there is not.

Cliff. Happy Blandish! your triumph is evident.

Lady E. Blandish, the odious creature—He is my abhorrence—You are hardly worse yourself in my bad opinion, though you have done so much more to deserve it.

Cliff. How cruel are the circumstances that compel me to leave you under these impressions!—nay—more—at such a time to urge a request, that during your most favourable thoughts of me would have appeared strange if not presumptuous.—This is the key of my apartment. It contains a secret that the exigency of the hour obliged me, against inclination or propriety, to lodge there. Should Sir Clement return before me, I implore you to prevent his discovery, and give to what you find within, your confidence and protection. Lord Gayville—but I shall go too far—the most anxious event of my life presses on me. I conjure you to comply, by all the compassion and tenderness nature has treasured in your heart—not for me—but for occasions worthy their display. Pray take it.

[*Gives the Key, which she receives with some reluctance and exit.*

Lady E. Heigho!—It's well, he's gone without insisting on my answer: I was in a sad flutter of indecision. What mysterious means he takes to engage me in a confidence which I could not directly accept!—I am to find a letter, I suppose—the story of his heart—Its errors and defence—My brother's name, also—to furnish me with a new interest in the secret, and one I might avow— One may dislike this art, but must be sensible of his delicacy——Ah, when these two qualities unite in a man, I am afraid he is an overmatch for the wisest of us—Hark!—sure that is the sound of my uncle's coach— [*Looks out of the Window.*] 'Tis he—and now for the secret—Curiosity! innate irresistible principle in womankind, be my excuse, before I dare question my mind upon other motives.

[*Exit.*

SCENE IV.

Another Apartment.

Enter LADY EMILY.

Lady E. Oh, lud! I could hardly tremble more at opening this man's apartment, were there a possibility of finding him within side. How do people find courage to do a wrong thing, when an innocent discovery cannot be prosecuted without such timidity?

[*Approaches the Door timidly, and unlocks it.*

Enter MISS ALTON.

Amazement! Miss Alton! what is all this?

Miss Alton. Madam, I was brought here, for an hour's concealment; who I really am, I would not, if possible to avoid it, divulge in this house. When you saw me last, you honoured me with a favourable opinion—My story, not explained at full, might subject me to doubts, that would shake your candour.

Lady E. What shall I do?—She is pale, and ready to faint—I cannot let her be exposed in such a situation.—Retire—you may rely upon me for present security—You know best your pretensions to my future opinion.— [*Hearing* Sir Clement.] —Begone, or you are discovered.

[*Shuts her in, and locks* Clifford *'s Door.*

Enter Sir Clement.

Sir C. Oh, the triumph of honour! Oh, the sincerity of friendship! How my opinions are ratified—how my system is proved!

Lady E. Oh, spirits, spirits, forsake me not!—Oh, for a moment's dissimulation!

Sir C. There are some, now, who would feed moroseness and misanthropy with such events: to me they give delight, as convictions and warnings to mankind.

Lady E. Of how superior a quality, my good uncle, must be the benevolence you possess! it rises with the progress of mischief; and is gratified (upon principles of general good) by finding confidence abused, and esteem misplaced. Am I not right in attributing your joy at present to that sort of refinement?

Sir C. Hah! and to what sensations, my good niece, shall be attributed the present state of your spirits? To the disgust you took to Clifford almost at first sight. It will not be with indifference, but pleasure, you will hear of his turning out the veriest rascal, the most complete impostor, the most abandoned—but hold, hold!—I must not wrong him by superlatives—he is matched too.

Lady E. Really!—I congratulate you upon such a check of charity.

Sir C. And I wish you joy, my pretty pert one, upon the credit your sex has acquired, in producing this other chef-d'œuvre—such a composition of the highest vices and the lowest—But your goodnature will, I dare say, easily find palliatives for both parties.

Lady E. Come, sir; no more of your sarcasms. I can treat wrong actions with levity, and yet consider them with detestation. Prudes and pretenders condemn with austerity. To the collection of suspicions you are master of, let me add one—In a young lady, of the delicacy and age you have described, always suspect the virtue that does not wear a smile.

Sir C. And the sincerity that wears one awkwardly.

Enter PROMPT, *hastily.*

Prompt. Joy to your honour; I see you have caught her.

Sir C. Her!—whom?

Prompt. [LADY EMILY *turning.*] I ask your ladyship's pardon—Having only the glimpse of a petticoat, and knowing the object of my chase was in this house, I confess I mistook you.

Sir C. In this house?

Prompt. As sure as we are—She came in through the garden, under Mr. Clifford's arm—up the other stairs, I suppose.—If my lady had been hereabouts, she must have seen her.

Lady E. [*In confusion.*] Yes; but, unluckily, I was quite out of the way.

Sir C. Such audaciousness passes credibility.—Emily, what do you think of him?

Lady E. That he is a monster.— [*Aside.*] How my dilemmas multiply!

Sir C. What, to my house! to his apartment here! I wonder he did not ask for protection in yours.—What should you have said?

Lady E. I don't know; but, had I been so imposed upon as to receive her, I should scorn to betray even the criminal I had engaged to protect.

Sir C. [*Tries at the Door, and finds it locked.*] Emily, my dear, do ring the bell, to know if the housekeeper has a second key to this lock.

Lady E. What shall I do?

Prompt. She is certainly there, sir, and cannot escape. Where can she better remain, till you can assemble all parties, confront them, face to face, and bring every thing that has passed to a full explanation?

Sir C. With all my heart; send and collect every body concerned as fast as possible.—How I long for so complicated an exhibition of the purity of the human heart; Come with me, Emily, and help to digest my plan,—Friends and lovers, what a scene shall we show you!

[*Takes* LADY EMILY *under the Arm.—Exeunt.*]

ACT THE FIFTH.

SCENE I.

An Apartment.

Enter CLIFFORD *and* MR. RIGHTLY.

Cliff. Your knowledge in the profession, Mr. Rightly, is as unquestionable as your integrity; but there is something so surprising in the recovery of the Charlton estate.—If you knew, too, how the value of the acquisition is enhanced, by the opportune moment in which it presents itself—I am in too much emotion to thank you as I ought.

Rightly. Sir, I want neither compliment, nor acknowledgment, for revealing what I should be a party to dishonesty to conceal.

Cliff. You have a right to all my thoughts: but I have an appointment to obey, that admits no time for explanation; favour me for a moment with your pencil, [RIGHTLY *takes out a Pencil and Pocket-book.*] and a blank page in that memorandum-book.

[CLIFFORD *writes.*

Rightly. My life on't, his head is turned upon some girl not worth a shilling —There is an amiable defect, but a very observable one, in the nature of some men. A good head and heart operate as effectually as vice or folly could do to make them improvident.

Cliff. Mr. Rightly, I confide to your hands a new secret relative to the Charlton estate; do not read it till you return home. [*Gives the Book, aside, and going.*] There, Gayville, is one reply to your challenge—and now for another.

Rightly. One moment, sir—I engage for no secrecy that my own judgment shall not warrant.

Cliff. And the benevolence of your heart approve—Those are my conditions.

[*Exeunt on opposite Sides.*

SCENE II.

Hyde Park.

Enter Lord Gayville *impetuously, looking at
his Watch.*

Lord G. Not here! I am sure I marked the hour as well as the place, precisely in my note. [*Walks about.*] Had I been told three days ago, that I should have been the appellant in a premeditated duel, I should have thought it an insult upon my principles—That Clifford should be the cause of my transgressing the legal and sacred duties, we have ever both maintained—oh, it would have seemed a visionary impossibility—But he comes, to cut reflections short—

Enter Clifford.

Lord G. I waited for you, sir.

Cliff. [*Bows in Silence.*]

Lord G. That ceremonial would grace an encounter of punctilio, but applies ill to the terms upon which I have called you here.

Cliff. What terms are those, my lord?

Lord G. Vengeance! Ample, final vengeance! Draw, sir.

Cliff. No, my lord; my sword is reserved for more becoming purposes: It is not the instrument of passion; and has yet been untried in a dispute with my friend.

Lord G. But why is it not ready for a different trial, the vindication of perfidy, the blackest species of perfidy, that ever the malignant enemy of mankind infused into the human breast—perfidy to the friend who loved and trusted you, and in the nearest interests of his heart.

Cliff. Take care, my lord; should my blood boil like yours, and it is rising fast, you know not the punishment that awaits you. I came temperate, your gross provocation and thirst of blood make temperance appear disgrace—I am tempted to take a revenge—

Lord G. [*Draws.*] The means are ready. Come, sir, you are to give an example of qualities generally held incompatible—bravery and dishonour.

Cliff. Another such a word, and by Heaven!—How have I deserved this opinion?

Lord G. Ask your conscience—Under the mask of friendship you have held a secret intercourse with the woman I adore; you have supplanted me in her affections, you have robbed me of the very charm of my life—can you deny it?

Cliff. I avow it all.

Lord G. Unparalleled insolence of guilt!

Cliff. Are you sure there is nothing within the scope of possibility that would excuse or atone—

Lord G. Death—Death only—no abject submission—no compromise for infamy—chuse instantly—and save yourself from the only stretch of baseness left—the invention of falsehood to palliate.—

Cliff. [*In the utmost Agitation, and drawing his Sword.*] Falsehood!— You shall have no other explanation.— [*After a Struggle within himself,* CLIFFORD *drops the Point, and exposes his Breast.*]

Lord G. Stand upon your defence, sir—What do you mean?

Cliff. You said nothing but my life would satisfy you, take it, and remember me.

Lord G. I say so still—but upon an equal pledge—I am no assassin.

Cliff. [*With great Emotion.*] If to strike at the heart of your friend, more deeply than that poor instrument in your hand could do, makes an assassin, you have been one already.

Lord G. That look, that tone, how like to innocence! Had he not avowed such abominable practices—

Cliff. I avow them again: I have rivalled you in the love of the woman you adore—her affections are riveted to me. I have removed her from your sight; secured her from your recovery—

Lord G. Damnation!

Cliff. I have done it to save unguarded beauty; to save unprotected innocence; to save—a sister.

Lord G. A sister!

Cliff. [*With Exultation.*] Vengeance! Ample, final vengeance! [*A Pause.*] It is accomplished—over him—and over myself—my victory is complete.

Lord G. Where shall I hide my shame!

Cliff. We'll share it, and forget it here.

[*Embraces.*

Lord G. Why did you keep the secret from me?

Cliff. I knew it not myself, till the strange concurrence of circumstances, to which you were in part witness a few hours since, brought it to light. I meant to impart to you the discovery, when my temper took fire—Let us bury our mutual errors in the thought, that we now for life are friends.

Lord G. Brothers, Clifford—Let us interchange that title, and doubly, doubly ratify it. Unite me to your charming sister; accept the hand of Lady Emily in return—her heart I have discovered to be yours——We'll leave the world to the sordid and the tasteless; let an Alscrip, or a Sir Clement Flint, wander after the phantom of happiness, we shall find her real retreat, and hold her by the bonds she covets, virtue, love, and friendship.

Cliff. Not a word more, my lord, the bars against your proposal are insuperable.

Lord G. What bars?

Cliff. Honour! Propriety—and pride.

Lord G. Pride, Clifford!

Cliff. Yes, my lord; Harriet Clifford shall not steal the hand of a prince; nor will I—though doting on Lady Emily with a passion like your own, bear the idea of a clandestine union in a family, to whom I am bound by obligation and trust. Indeed, my lord, without Sir Clement's consent, you must think no more of my sister.

Lord G. Stern stoic, but I will, and not clandestinely; I'll instantly to Sir Clement.

Cliff. Do not be rash; Fortune, or some better agent, is working in wonders —Meet me presently at your uncle's; in the mean while promise not to stir in this business.

Lord G. What hope from delay?

Cliff. Promise—

Lord G. I am in a state to catch at shadows——I'll try to obey you.

Cliff. Farewell!——

[*Exeunt.*

SCENE III.

Sir Clement's House.

Enter Miss Alscrip, in great Spirits, followed by Mrs. Blandish.

Miss Als. I am delighted at this summons from Sir Clement, Blandish; poor old clear-sight, I hope he has projected a reconciliation.

Mrs. Blandish. How I rejoice to see those smiles returned to the face that was made for them!

Miss Als. Returned, Blandish? I desire you will not insinuate it ever was without them—Why sure, you would not have the world imagine the temper of an heiress of my class, was to be ruffled by the loss of a paltry earl—I have been highly diverted with what has passed from beginning to end.

Mrs. Blandish. Well, if good humour can be a fault, sure the excess you carry it to must be the example.

Miss Als. I desire it may be made known in all companies, that I have done nothing but laugh—nay, it is true too.

Mrs. Blandish. My dear creature, of what consequence is the truth, when you are charging me with the execution of your desires?

Miss Als. But did you remember the airs of the moppet—Could any thing be more ridiculous?

Mrs. Blandish. The rivalship you mean——Rival Miss Alscrip.—He! he! he!

[*Half laugh.*

Miss Als. Yes, but when you take this tone in public, laugh a little louder.

Mrs. Blandish. Rival Miss Alscrip, ha! ha! ha!

Both. Ha! ha! ha! ha! ha! ha!

Mrs. Blandish. [*Wiping her Eyes, as not quite recovered from her Laugh.*] For mirth's sake, what is become of the rival?—Whom will you chuse she shall have run away with?

Miss Als. Leave it in doubt as it is; fixing circumstances confines the curiosity to one story which may be disproved; uncertainty leaves it open to a hundred, and makes them all probable. But I hear some of the company upon the stairs: Now, Blandish—You shall be witness to the temper and dignity, with which a woman of my consequence can discard a quality courtship that offends her—

Mrs. Blandish. Sweet tempered soul!

Enter Sir Clement Flint.

Sir C. Miss Alscrip, your—

[*As he is beginning to say your humble Servant,*

Enter BLANDISH *out of Breath.*

Blandish. The duel's over.

Sir C. And the parties unhurt—You are too late in your intelligence by some minutes. But I know you must rejoice [*Ironically.*] from your attachment to all parties.—Miss Alscrip, your very—

Miss Als. Duel!—Pray let us hear the particulars—As there is no mischief, I shall not faint.

[*Ironically.*

Sir C. I guess it has been of the common-place kind.—Hats over the brows —glum silence—thrust—parry—and riposte——Explain and shake hands: Your man of honour never sets his friend right, till he has exchanged a shot— or a thrust: Oh, a little steel recipe is a morning whet to the temper: It carries off all qualms, and leaves the digestion free for any thing that is presented to it.

Miss Als. Dear, how fortunate! Considering the pills some folks have to swallow.

Sir C. Blandish, see if the door of Clifford's room is yet unlocked, there is a person within you little expect to find, and whom it may be proper for this lady and me to interrogate together.

[*The Door opens, and*

Enter LADY EMILY.

Blandish. Lady Emily!

Sir C. Inexplicable, with a vengeance.

Miss Als. [*Aside.*] Lady Emily, shut up in Clifford's apartment! Beyond my expectation, indeed.

[*With a malicious Air.*

[LADY EMILY *seems pleased.*

Sir C. [*Dryly.*] Lady Emily, I know you were always cautious whom you visited, and never gave a better proof of your discernment.

Lady E. Never. Oh! my poor dear uncle, you little think what is going to befall you.

Sir C. Not a disappointment in love, I hope.

Lady E. No, but in something much nearer your heart—your system is threatened with a blow, that I think, and from my soul I hope, it never will recover: would you guess that the sagacious observations of your whole life are upon the point of being confounded by the production—

Sir C. Of what?

Lady E. A woman of ingenuous discretion, and a man of unaffected integrity.

Sir C. Hah!

Mrs. Blandish. What can she mean?

Miss Als. Nothing good—she looks so pleasant.

Lady E. Come forth, my injured friend. Our personal acquaintance has been short, but our hearts were intimate from the first sight.   [*Presenting her.*] Your prisoner, sir, is Miss Harriet Clifford.

Sir C. Clifford's sister!

Miss Als. What, the run-away Alton, turned into a sprig of quality.

Lady E. [*Disdainfully to* Miss Alscrip .] The humble dependent of Alscrip house—The wanton—the paragon of fraud—the only female that can equal Clifford. [*Tauntingly to* Sir Clement .] She is indeed!

[*With Emphasis and Affection.*

Blandish. [*Aside.*] Oh, rot the source of the family fondness—I see I have no card left in my favour—but the heiress.   [*Goes to her and pays Court —During this Conversation, aside,* Lady Emily *seems encouraging* Miss Clifford .— Sir Clement *musing, and by Turns examining her.*]

Sir C. [*To himself.*] "Ingenuous discretion!"

Enter Clifford, *and runs to his Sister.*

Cliff. My dearest Harriet! the joy I purposed in presenting you here, is anticipated: but, my blameless fugitive! when your story is known, my pride in you will not be a wonder.—Miss Clifford, behold your persecutor and your convert.

Enter Lord Gayville.

Lord G. [*With Rapture.*] Her persecutor and her convert. Her virtues, which no humility could conceal, and every trial made more resplendent, discovered, disgraced, and reclaimed a libertine.—

Miss Cliff. How am I distressed!—what ought I to answer?

Lord G. Impressed sentiment upon desire, gave honour to passion, and drew from my soul a vow, which Heaven chastise me when I violate, to obtain her by a legal, sacred claim, or renounce fortune, family and friends, and become a self-devoted outcast of the world.

Miss Cliff. Oh! brother, interpose.

Sir C. My lord, your fortune, family and friends are much obliged to you. Your part is perfect—Mr. Clifford, you are called upon. Miss, in strict propriety, throws the business upon her relations—Come, finish the comedy, join one of her hands to the gallant's, while, with the other, she covers her blushes—and he in rapture delivers the moral. All for Love, or, the World well lost.

[Miss CLIFFORD *still appears agitated.*

Cliff. Be patient, my Harriet, this is the school for prejudice, and the lesson of its shame is near.

Miss Als. I vow these singular circumstances give me quite a confusion of pleasure. The astonishing good fortune of my late protegee, in finding so impassioned a friendship in her brother's bed-chamber; the captivating eloquence of Lord Gayville, in winding up an eclaircissement which I admire —not for the first time—to-day—and the superlative joy Sir Clement must feel at an union, founded upon the purity of the passions,—are subjects of such different congratulation, that I hardly know where to begin.

Lady E. [*Aside*] Charming! her insolence will justify what so seldom occurs to one—a severe retort, without a possible sense of compunction.

Miss Als. But in point of fortune—don't imagine, Sir Clement, I would insinuate that the lady is destitute—oh Lord, far from it. Her musical talents are a portion—

ALSCRIP *and* RIGHTLY *without.*

Alscrip. Why, stop a moment—

Sir C. What have we here—the lawyers in dispute?

Alscrip. [*Entering.*] You have not heard my last word yet.

Rightly. [*Entering.*] You have heard mine, sir.

Alscrip. [*Whispering.*] I'll make the five thousand I offered, ten.

Rightly. Millions would not bribe me— [*Coming forward.*] When I detect wrong, and vindicate the sufferer, I feel the spirit of the law of England, and the pride of a practitioner.

Alscrip. Lucifer confound such practices! [*In this Part of the Scene,* SIR CLEMENT, LORD GAYVILLE, LADY EMILY, CLIFFORD, *and* MISS CLIFFORD, *form one Group.*]

[RIGHTLY *opens a Deed, and points out a Part*
of it to SIR CLEMENT.]

[MR. *and* MISS ALSCRIP *carry on the*
following Speeches on the Side at which
ALSCRIP *has entered. And* MR. *and* MRS.
BLANDISH *are farther back, observing.*]

Alscrip. That cursed! cursed flaw.—

Miss Als. Flaw! who has dared to talk of one? not in my reputation, sir?

Alscrip. No, but in my estate; which is a damned deal worse.

Miss Als. How? what? when?—where?——The estate that was to be
settled upon me?

Alscrip. Yes, but that *me* turned topsey turvey—when *me* broke into my
room this morning, and the devil followed, to fly away with all my faculties at
once—I am ruined—Let us see what you will settle upon your poor father.

Miss Als. I settle upon you?

Mrs. Blandish. This is an embarrassing accident.

Miss Als. Yes, and a pretty help you are, with a drop chin, like a
frontispiece to the Lamentations.

Rightly. [*Coming forward with* SIR CLEMENT.] I stated this with some
doubt this morning, but now my credit as a lawyer upon the issue.—The
heiress falls short of the terms in your treaty by two thousand pounds a-year
—which this deed, lately and providentially discovered, entails upon the heirs
of Sir William Charlton, and consequently, in right of his mother, upon this
gentleman.

Lady E. How!

Lord G. Happy disappointment.

Sir C. [*Aside.*] Two thousand a-year to Clifford! It's a pity, for the parade
of disinterestedness, that he opened his designs upon Emily, before he knew
his pretensions.

Lady E. [*Aside.*] Now, if there were twenty ceilings, and as many floors,
could not I find a spot to settle my silly looks upon.

[SIR CLEMENT *observes her with his usual Shyness.*

Sir C. [*Turning towards* ALSCRIP.] Palm a false title upon me? I should have thought the attempt beyond the collective assurance of Westminster-hall —and he takes the loss as much to heart as if he bought the estate with his own money.

Alscrip. [*With Hesitation.*] Sir Clement—what think you—of an amicable adjustment of all these businesses?

Sir C. [*Ironically.*] Nothing can be more reasonable. The value of Miss Alscrip's amiable disposition, placed against the abatement of her fortune, is a matter of the most easy computation; and to decide the portion, Mr. Clifford ought to relinquish of his acquisition—Lady Emily—will you be a referée?

Lady E. [*Aside.*] Yes, the lynx has me—I thought I should not escape. — [*To him.*] No, sir; my poor abilities only extend to an amicable endeavour here. [*To* MISS ALSCRIP *.*] And really, Miss Alscrip, I see no reason for your being dispirited; there may be many ready-made titles at market, within the reach of your purse. Or, why should not a woman of your consequence originate her own splendour? there's an old admirer of mine—He would make a very pretty lord—and indeed, would contribute something on his own part, to ease the purchase—The Blandish family is well with all administrations, and a new coronet is always as big again as an old one. I don't see how you could lay out part of your independency to more advantage.

Blandish. [*Aside.*] Yes, but since flaws are in fashion, I shall look a little into things before I agree to the bargain.

Miss Als. [*Aside.*] I'll die before I'll discover my vexation—and yet, [*Half crying.*] no title—no place.

Lady E. Depend upon it, Miss Alscrip, your place will be found exactly where it ought to be. The public eye, in this country, is never long deceived— Believe me—and cherish obscurity—Title may bring forward merits, but it also places our defects in horrid relief.

Alscrip. Molly, the sooner we get out of court the better—we have damnably the worst of this cause, so come along, Molly— [*Taking her under the Arm.*] —and farewell to Berkeley Square. Whoever wants Alscrip House, will find it in the neighbourhood of Furnival's Inn, with the noble title of Scrivener, in capitals—Blank bonds at the windows, and a brass knocker at the door. [*Pulling her.*] Come along, Molly.

Miss Als. [*Half crying.—Aside.*] Oh! the barbarous metamorphosis—but his flusterums for a week, will serve my temper, as a regimen. I will then take the management of my affairs into my own hands, and break from my cloud anew: and you shall find [*To the Company.*] there are those without a coronet, that can be as saucy, and as loud, and stop the way in all public places, as well as the best of you. [LADY EMILY *laughs.*] Yes, madam, and without borrowing your ladyship's airs.

Als. [*Pulling her.*] Come along, Molly.

Miss Als. Oh you have been a jewel of a father.

[*The Company laugh.*

[*Exeunt* MR. *and* MISS ALSCRIP.

[MR. *and* MRS. BLANDISH *stay behind.*

Lady E. Mrs. Blandish, sure you do not leave your friend, Miss Alscrip, in distress?

Mrs. Blandish. We'll not disturb the ashes of the dead—my sweet Lady Emily—

Blandish. Oh my sweet sister, none of your flourishes—In the present mood of the company, even mine would not do. Truth and sentiment have the ascendency. But let them alone; and they'll come round again. [*Addressing the Company.*] Flattery is the diet of good humour; and not one of you can live without it; and when you quarrel with the family of Blandish, you only leave refined cookery, to be fed upon scraps, by a poor cousin or a led captain.

[*Taking his Sister under his Arm.*

Mrs. Blandish. [*With a Look of Courtship to the Company.*] Oh! the two charming pairs!

Blandish. [*Pulling her away.*] Oh! thou walking dedication!

[*Exeunt.*

Lord G. Precious group, fare ye well. [*To* SIR CLEMENT .] And now, sir, whatever may be your determinations towards me—here are pretensions you may patronize without breach of discretion. The estate which devolves to my friend—

Rightly. To prevent errors—is not his to bestow.

Sir C. What now—more flaws?

Rightly. The estate was his beyond the reach of controversy: but before he was truly sure of it, on his way to Hyde-Park, did this spendthrift, by a stroke of his pen, divest himself of every shilling—Here is the covenant by which he binds himself to execute proper conveyances as soon as the necessary forms can be gone through.

Lord G. And in favour of whom is this desperate act?

Rightly. Of a most dangerous seducer—a little mercenary, that, when she gets hold of the heart, does not leave an atom of it our own.

All. How!

Rightly. [*With Feeling.*] And there she stands, [*Pointing to* Miss Clifford .] with a look and an emotion that would condemn her before any court in the universe.

Lady E. Glorious—matchless Clifford!

Miss Cliff. Brother, this must not be.

Cliff. Your pardon, my dear Harriet, it is done. Sir Clement, my sister's fortune is still far short of what you expected with Miss Alscrip; for that deficiency, I have only to offer the virtues Lord Gayville has proved, and the affection she found it easier to control, than to conceal. If you will receive her, thus circumstanced, into your family, mine has been an acquisition indeed.

Lady E. [*Coming up to* Sir Clement .] Now, sir, where's the suspicion! Where is now the ruling principle that governs mankind! Through what perspective, by what trial, will you find self-interest here? What, not one pithy word to mock my credulity!—Alas! poor Yorick—quite chop-fallen.— Forgive me, sir, I own I am agitated to extravagance—You found me disconcerted at the first discovery; I am delighted at the last; there's a problem of my disposition worthy your solving.

Sir C. [*Who has been profoundly thoughtful.*] Mr. Rightly, favour me with that paper in your hand.

Rightly. Mr. Clifford's engagement, sir. [*Gives the Paper:* Sir Clement *looks it over, and tears it.*] What do you mean, sir?

Sir C. To cancel the obligation, and pay the equivalent to Gayville; or if Clifford will have his own way, and become a beggar by renewing it, to make an heiress of my own for his reparation—and there she stands. [*Pointing to* Lady Emily .] With sensibility and vivacity so uncommonly blended, that they extract benevolence wherever it exists, and create it where it never was before—Your point is carried—You may both fall upon your knees, for the consent of the ladies.

Lord G. [*To* Miss Clifford .] In this happy moment, let my errors be forgot, and my love alone remembered.

Miss Cliff. With these sanctions for my avowal—I will not deny that I saw and felt the sincerity of your attachment, from the time it was capable of being restrained by respect.

Cliff. Words are wanting, Lady Emily—

Lady E. I wish they may with all my heart, but it is generally remarked that wanting words, is the beginning of a florid set speech—To be serious, Clifford—We want but little explanation on either side—Sir Clement will tell you how long we have conversed by our actions. [*Gives her Hand.*] My dear uncle, how a smile becomes you in its natural meaning!

Sir C. If you think me a convert, you are mistaken: I have ever believed *self* to be the predominant principle of the human mind—My heart at this instant confirms the doctrine—There's my problem for yours, my dear Emily, and may all who hear me agree in this solution—to reward the deserving, and make those we love happy, is self-interest in the extreme.

THE END.

THE DRAGON TATTOO BOOK

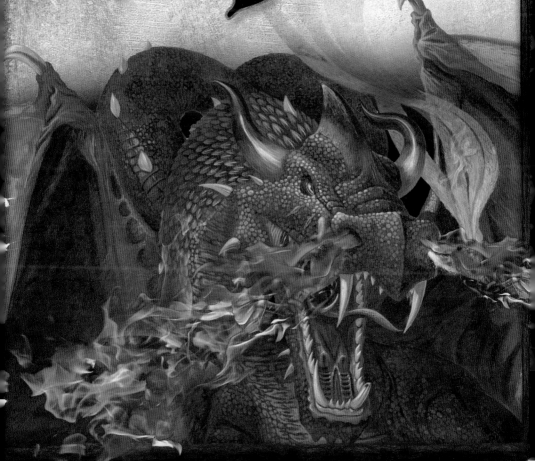

This is a Carlton book

Text and artwork copyright.
© 2011 Carlton Books Limited
Design copyright © 2011 Carlton Books Limited

Published in 2011 by Carlton Books Limited, an
imprint of the Carlton Publishing Group,
20 Mortimer Street, London, W1T 3JW.

10 9 8 7 6 5 4 3 2 1

A catalogue record for this book is
available from the British Library.

ISBN: 978-1-84732-773-4
Printed and bound in China.

Picture Credits

The publishers would like to thank the following
sources for their kind permission to reproduce the
pictures in this book.

Key to picture credits:
t: top, b: bottom, l: left, r: right, c: centre

Bone Clones, Inc: 15bl, 15br, 15bc, 18b; Corbis
/DK Limited: 29b, /Don Mason: 13br; Getty
Images/Bridgeman Art Library: 9, 14; iStockphoto.
com: 4, 6r, 28, /Linda Bucklin: 20, 23, 24, /Qizhi
He: 21, /Stefan Weichelt: 13tr, 19; Natural History
Museum: 18r; The Bridgeman Art Library/Wayne
Anderson: 25 br; Thinkstock/Hemera: 6l, 7tr, 7l,
7br, 10, 11b, 12cl, 12cr, 12br, 15r, 17, 25tr, 26bl,
27, 29t, /iStockphoto: 11t, 12bl, 26r.
All other illustrations: © Carlton Books.

Every effort has been made to acknowledge correctly
and contact the source and/or copyright holder of
each picture and Carlton Books Limited apologises for
any unintentional errors or omissions which will be
corrected in future editions of this book.

Tattoo safety information:

Carlton Books Limited, an imprint of the Carlton Publishing Group,
20 Mortimer Street, London, W1T 3JW.

JFM MJJASOND/11/6729 Printed in Dongguan, China.

Product function: removable temporary tattoos.
Tattoo ingredients: Acrylic Resin, Synthetic Iron Oxide pigment (Black)/CI 77499, FD&C Yellow
No. 5 Aluminium Lake/CI 19140, FD&C Yellow No. 6 Aluminium Lake/CI 15985, FD&C Blue
No. 1 Aluminium Lake/CI 42090, D&C Red No. 7 Aluminium
Lake/CI 15850.

WARNING: Not suitable for children under 36 months due
to small parts. Choking hazard. Use by April 2013.

Do not apply on lips or around the eyes. If the product
causes irritation, wash the skin immediately. If symptoms
continue, seek medical advice.

Eczema-type reactions could potentially occur
among users who have previously been sensitised to
FD&C Yellow No. 5 Aluminium Lake/CI 19140

Conforms to ASTM F-963-08, ASTM D4236
and EN71 safety requirements.

Project Editor: Paul Virr
Writer: Paul Virr
Designers: Joanne Mitchell, Ceri Woods
Creative Director: Clare Baggaley
Production: Claire Halligan

THE DRAGON TATTOO BOOK

CARLTON KIDS

Here be Dragons!

Our world is filled with dragons, but they are rarely seen. Skilled dragon spotters are sensitive to the slightest clue – a glint seen from the corner of your eye could be a dragon sliding silently out of sight.

The Mysterious Dragon

Dragons are mysterious creatures with incredible magical powers. Nobody knows their true origins, but dragons are much older than humankind. Indeed, legends of dragons go right back to the very dawn of history.

Dragons usually blend into the landscape, but every now and then you might catch the outline of a dragon against the sky.

Hidden Dragons

Dragons are not as common today as they once were, but they still lurk in the remote corners of our world. Over the ages many adventurers have tried to kill or tame the dragon. This is why dragons prefer to remain hidden from human eyes.

Legends are filled with the adventures of fearless dragonslayers, such as Beowulf.

YOUR DRAGON TATTOOS

This book comes with a sheet of dragon tattoos in different magical designs — all guaranteed to be resistant to dragon fire! See if you can find these fearsome dragon tattoos on your tattoo sheet.

VULCANIAN FIRE DRAGON

BARB-TAILED SAVANNAH DRAGON

FIVE-CLAWED SERPENT DRAGON

DRAGON SKULL

Follow the instructions on the back of the tattoo sheet to apply your tattoos.

Dragon Spotting

Dragons are secretive creatures, but if you are patient, and you know what to look for, you might be lucky enough to spot one. To help you with dragon spotting, here's a quick guide to the most common types of dragon.

Mountain Dragons

Mountain dragons are common in Central and Eastern Europe, where they make their lairs on mountain tops or high cliff ledges. They have strong, gripping claws that help them cling to rock faces.

Serpent Dragons

All dragons are dangerous, but serpent dragons are doubly so as they have a poisonous bite that can kill instantly. Common in India and China, this species is also known for its strong magical powers.

Forest Dragons

There are many types of forest dragon, from small woodland dragons no bigger than a bird of prey, through to giant forest species that make their nests from giant tree trunks. They are generally green in colour.

Water Dragons

Many dragons inhabit the watery regions of the world. Sea dragons are so big that they can be mistaken for islands. Freshwater dragons lurk beneath the surface of rivers and lakes.

Ice Dragons

The hot blood of the ice dragon helps it to survive in the coldest of climates. Ice dragons, with their white or silvery scales, are usually found in the frozen parts of our planet.

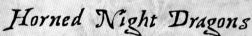

TRIPLE-HORNED NIGHT DRAGON

Horned Night Dragons

Horned dragons are numerous, but one of the hardest to spot is the Horned Night Dragon, which only ever leaves its lair under the cover of complete darkness.

The dark colour of this Horned Night Dragon makes it very tricky to spot at night.

Dragon's Den

Dragons make their homes in many different places. Dark caverns, towering cliffs or even hollow trees might hide a dragon's lair. But beware, very few have set foot in a dragon's lair and lived to tell the tale!

Home Sweet Home

A cave in a lonely spot is almost certain to be a dragon's den, but dragon homes come in all shapes and sizes. Some large dragons build gigantic nests. Small dragons, such as the Black Dwarf Dragon, live in tiny burrows.

Mountain Dragons make their homes high up in the mountains or even on the slopes of volcanoes.

This ancient picture shows a Forest Dragon using its tail to mark out where it will build its nest.

A dragon will often sleep right on top of its precious treasure hoard.

Treasure Hunt

Dragons love to collect shiny and precious things, such as jewels and gold. They keep a watchful eye on their treasure hoard, so only the brave or the foolhardy would enter a dragon's den to steal it!

Fire and Ice

Dragons are hardy and adaptable creatures. They can live in a wide range of different habitats, from scorching deserts to ice–capped mountains. Some of the rarest dragons can be found in extreme places.

Some Like It Hot

Many dragons live in the hottest parts of the globe. But the most extreme heat-loving dragon is the Laki Lava Dragon, which makes its home in the crater of a live volcano!

LAKI LAVA DRAGON

This Laki Lava Dragon likes to bathe in lakes of boiling lava.

Chilling Out

One of the reasons that dragons like to live in harsh and lonely places, is that they are unlikely to be disturbed by dragon hunters. The ice caves of Antarctica are home to many dragons that thrive in sub-zero temperatures.

ANTARCTIC SNOW DRAGON

An Antarctic Snow Dragon makes its way home to its ice cavern lair.

Super Senses

Dragons have powerful eyesight and can see clearly over great distances. They also have sensitive hearing and can pick up a whisper carried on the breeze. Their sense of smell is amazing too, which is very useful for sniffing out prey.

The Dragon's Gaze

Always avoid the gaze of a dragon. Its chilling stare can put you into a trance so that you will be unable to hide secrets from it. This could be very dangerous if you were planning to steal its treasure!

Never be tempted to test the power of the dragon's gaze — it could prove fatal.

Eye Spy

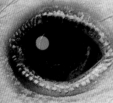

The Green Forest Dragon has a wide pupil for peering through the gloom under a forest canopy.

The Bog Dragon's eyes are all you might spot if it is lurking beneath the surface of a swamp.

Water dragons have a transparent eyelid to help them see clearly when they are underwater.

The Triple-horned Desert Dragon has a vertical eye pupil to protect it from the glare of the sun.

Deadly Hunters

Dragons use their amazing senses of sight, smell and hearing to detect unsuspecting prey from afar. They wait motionless until their victim is in range and then strike with lightning speed.

EYE OF THE DRAGON

A Barb-tailed Savannah Dragon swoops from a mountaintop to seize its prey.

Dragons can sense buried gold nuggets or even a single gold coin in someone's pocket!

The Sixth Sense

Dragons possess a sixth sense — the ability to detect gold. Many treasure hunters have tried to use dragons to help them, but this has rarely ended well...

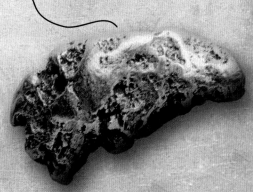

13

Scales and Teeth

A dragon's scales are as tough as steel armour to protect it from attack. They also help to keep the dragon's body at a normal temperature, whether it's sleeping in a fiery volcano or swimming in a frozen lake.

Tales of Scales

Dragons sometimes shed a scale or two. Scales are very rarely found, but are said to be magical. However, if one is used in a spell that might harm a dragon, it will burst into flames!

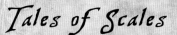

SIBERIAN FROST DRAGON SCALES

Dragon scales are flexible, fireproof and extremely tough.

The scales of the Silver Water Dragon shimmer like the surface of a lake and are completely waterproof.

Dragon Teeth

The jaws of a dragon are filled with frightening fangs. Some teeth are pointed like daggers, while others have razor-sharp edges or can even deliver a poisonous bite.

The dagger-like teeth of the Long-eared Serpent Dragon can bite straight through armour.

The jagged-edged tooth of the Arabian Sand Dragon.

The White-fanged Marsh Dragon's teeth are sharp and pointed.

The long front fangs of the Crystal Ice Dragon look like icicles.

Heads or Tails?

Whichever way you approach a dragon, it is a truly terrifying foe. As well as fangs and fiery breath, a dragon's head often has horns or antlers. Its tail is also a powerful weapon and can have deadly spikes.

The Horned Swamp Dragon has both long and shot horns on its very spiky head.

Horrible Horns

A dragon's horns or antlers are deadly in attack or defence. They are made of rock-hard bone and can grow very large. Dragons use their horns to kill prey, but also when fighting each other.

CURLY-HORNED MARSH DRAGON

The Spike-Tailed Night Dragon packs a deadly sting in its tail.

Terrible Tails

The dragon's tail is a frightening weapon which it uses to lash out at its enemies. Tails can be forked, arrow-tipped, spiked, or might even end in a bone-crushing club or a poisonous sting!

The Red Water Dragon can coil its tail around prey to crush the life out of it.

Killer Claws

A dragon's claws or talons are one of its great weapons. They usually have three or four claws on each hand or foot, though some water dragons have as many as five. Some species even have extra claws on their wing-tips.

Occasionally a dragon will shed a broken claw, but it is soon replaced.

Tough Stuff

Dragon claws are even harder than diamonds. This makes them useful for dragons who build their lairs by clawing out tunnels under the ground. Of course, they also make lethal weapons.

BLUE SERPENT DRAGON FOOT

Claws vary in shape, from long and curved, to short spikes like this thumb claw of the Black Ice Dragon.

Claw Spotters' Guide

Ice Dragons
Tiny talons give better grip on icy glaciers and make very sharp weapons too.

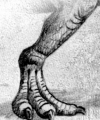

Savannah Dragons
Sharp, hooked claws are perfect for snatching prey from the grassy plains.

Swamp Dragons
Short hoof-like claws are good for swamps and scrambling up muddy slopes.

Serpent Dragons
Long fingers with grasping claws make these deadly dragons easy to recognize!

Razor Sharp

A dragon keeps its claws ultra-sharp, using rocks to sharpen each claw to a point. Dragons can hold delicate objects in their claws without breaking them, but those same claws can also deliver deadly, slashing swipes.

An African Mountain Dragon bears down on its prey with outstretched claws.

Dragon Fire

Not every dragon can breathe fire, but those that do are among the most dangerous. A quick burst of fire means instant death for the unfortunate victim. Longer bursts can easily melt swords, shields and armour!

Flame Over!

Dragon fire is a dragon's most powerful weapon. A quick blast of fire can scorch enemies who would otherwise be out of reach. An angry fire-breathing dragon can turn towns and villages to smouldering ruins in minutes.

Dragons have fireproof tongues and their scales protect them from their own flames.

Eastern Forest Dragons fight by shooting balls of fire at each other.

Burning Secret

Nobody knows how dragons actually produce fire. Some say their hearts are magically made of fire, which is also why their blood is hot. Dragons use fire sparingly as it takes a lot of energy to produce.

GOLDEN FIRE DRAGON

Dragon Eggs

Dragon eggs come in all shapes, sizes and colours. The female dragon takes care to lay her eggs somewhere safe as they take a very long time to hatch. Some baby dragons may not break out of their eggs for over a hundred years!

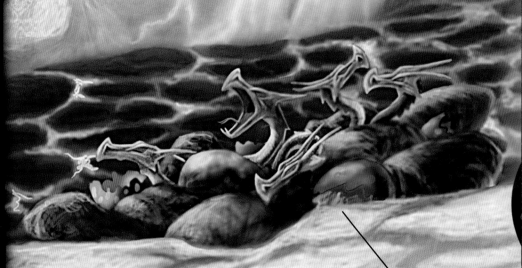

Extreme Eggs

Some dragons keep their eggs warm by curling their bodies around them in the lair. Vulcanian Fire Dragons lay their eggs close to the lava of a volcano, while ice dragons have to keep their eggs freezing cold to help them hatch!

Vulcanian Fire Dragon babies finally pop out of their eggs after about a hundred years inside a volcano.

ANTARCTIC SNOW DRAGON EGG

Dragon Babies

When a baby dragon is ready to hatch it makes a high-pitched sound and the egg shakes and cracks. Finally the shell breaks open and the little dragon pokes its head out to greet its mother.

Hatchlings look like smaller versions of their parents, but they have yet to learn to fly or breathe fire.

Youth and Age

Nobody knows just how long a dragon can live for. Many believe that it takes hundreds of years for a young hatchling to develop into a full-grown dragon.

A hatchling's small wings can barely lift it off the ground.

The baby dragon's horns are soft and flexible.

A dragon starts out with small baby teeth, but as it grows they are replaced with proper fangs.

GOLDEN FIRE DRAGON HATCHLING

The Baby Dragon

Baby dragons look like small versions of their parents, but their scales are soft and their wings are too small for flying. Baby dragons grow up very slowly and are always well-looked after by their mothers.

Young Dragons

When a dragon is old enough to hunt it is ready to leave the nest and build its own lair. Young dragons are proud and quick to anger, so they can be quite dangerous.

A young Spike-tongued Dragon stretches its wings as it prepares to fly from the nest.

A Dragon's Old Age

Elderly dragons can be huge as dragons never stop growing. They are less active and spend a lot of time alseep. Be careful of old dragons as they are still cunning and deadly.

Watch where you step — an elderly Mountain Fire Dragon can be as big as a mountain!

Magical Places

Dragons prefer to be alone, but they do gather together at certain times of the year in special magical places. Dragons fly in great flocks to these meetings.

Flock Together

Few people have seen a flock of dragons. Some claim to have heard the beating of many giant wings as dragons fly together in the dead of night.

Dragons of all shapes and sizes gather at magical spots such as ancient castles.

HOOK-BEAKED MOUNTAIN DRAGON

The Ruins of Drachenfels

One place that dragons return to every year is Drachenfels, a ruined castle where the dragon Fafnir was killed by the dragon-slayer Seigfried. Some think that the spilling of dragon blood has made Drachenfels a place of great magic.

Seigfried slayed Fafnir with a magical sword that could cut through solid iron.

The strange and haunting sound of dragon song can travel for many miles.

Dragon Song

Dragons sing strange and beautiful songs to guide other dragons to the places where they gather. These songs are in an ancient language that only dragons can still understand.

Dragon Spells

Dragons are magical creatures, which is why everything from a dragon's blood to its scales has been used by wizards and witches in their spells.

Powerful Potions

Many parts of the dragon are known to have magical powers, but they can be dangerous to use in a magical potion. Some wizards have met a sticky end by dabbling in dragon magic.

It is said that the famous wizard Merlin used dragon blood in his magic spells.

A dragon's blood is magically hot and never cools down.

DRAGON HEART

Burning Blood

Some ancient books of spells say that drinking dragon's blood will give you the power to see into the future. But take care not to drink too much or you might turn into a dragon!

Bones

Ground down to a fine powder, dragon bones are used in healing spells and potions to treat a range of illnesses.

The leg bone of an ancient dragon. People often mistake these rare finds for dinosaur fossils.

Dragon Slayers

Many brave adventurers have battled against dragons, but only a handful have ever defeated one. Here are a few of the most famous tales of dragon slayers and their bold deeds.

Saint George

The legend of Saint George tells how he slayed a dragon to rescue a princess. The dragon's scales were as strong as steel, but Saint George found a weak spot under its wing and pierced its heart with his lance.

Many knights in armour have battled with dragons, but Saint George is one of the most famous.

Marduk and Tiamat

An ancient story describes how a young god called Marduk set out to battle an evil female dragon called Tiamat. He had to use many weapons, including the power of thunder and lightning, to finally defeat her.

Marduk attacked the ferocious dragon with bolts of lightning.

DRAGON TOOTH

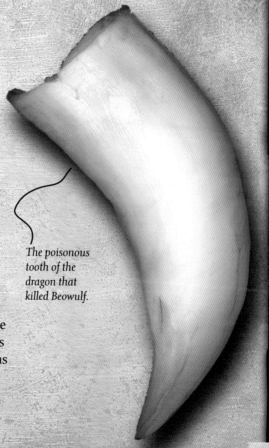

The poisonous tooth of the dragon that killed Beowulf.

Beowulf

The Anglo-Saxon king Beowulf heroically fought the dragon that attacked his kingdom, but during the battle it managed to bite him with its poisonous fangs. Even though he was dying, Beowulf managed to kill the dragon with his sword.

Dragon Lore!

Knowledge of dragons has been sought throughout the ages. Dragons guard their secrets carefully, so these few pages rescued from a rare and slightly scorched manuscript are extremely valuable.

The Dragon's Gaze

If you dare catch a dragon's eye,
Be wise and never tell a lie:
The dragon's gaze will clearly spy
Secrets you'd be wise to hide.

Dragon Gold

If you seek the dragon's gold,
Prepare to feel
Your blood run cold.
Every treasure has its price
And dragon gold
Might cost your life!

Dragon Spell

Those who spill a dragon's blood
And drink it down within the hour
Will gain these special magic powers:
To understand the speech of birds
And never more to feel the cold,
To see the truth behind the words
And feel the glow of hidden gold!